The
Immort*

PRESENTED BY

ALUMINUM COMPANY
OF AMERICA

The
Immortal Woodshed

Charles Martin Hall's Class Picture—Oberlin 1885

Junius Edwards

The
Immortal Woodshed

THE STORY OF THE INVENTOR
WHO BROUGHT ALUMINUM TO AMERICA

ILLUSTRATED BY EDWIN SCHMIDT

Dodd, Mead & Company   New York

 Contents

Sketches

The

Immortal Woodshed

1

. . . on December 6, 1863

DECEMBER SIXTH was cold in Dover, Ohio that frosty winter night. Outside the little parsonage the trees were tipped with snow. Inside the family living room, flames flickered in the broad fireplace and sent shadows dancing across the Rev. Mr. Hall's generous bookshelves. The cozy silence was occasionally punctured by a sharp report from a resin pocket in the burning logs.

A small boy lay stretched full length in front of the fire with elbows on the floor and chin resting on upturned palms. In front of him was an open book which kept his steady attention.

"Charlie, Charlie," called his mother from the kitchen. "You must go to bed now; you've had a long day."

"Just a minute, mama, I'm not sleepy yet. I want to read some more."

"All right, Charlie," his mother consented, "but only a few minutes."

2

Again Charlie, with his finger, traced out several sentences in his father's college chemistry. Then he raised his eyes from the fascinating pages and gazed through the dancing flames to the years when he would be old enough to experiment. Slowly his face slipped to the open book, his eyes closed, and he was sound asleep.

"Charlie, Charlie," called his mother again—but there was no answer. He was deep in his dreams.

Finally Sophronia Hall called to her husband, "Heman, find out what Charlie is doing. Even though he is six years old today, it's long past his bedtime."

The Rev. Mr. Hall came to the door and turned an indulgent eye on his sleeping son. His oldest child, George, was already following in his father's footsteps and studying for the ministry, but Charles was something of an enigma to him. There was a difference between the two boys which their father could not analyze. He could not foresee that Charles, growing into manhood, was to become more interested in the miracles of chemistry than in the mysteries of the churchmen. After a minute's meditation, Heman Hall shook his head in wonderment, tenderly took the sleeping boy in his arms and carried him up to bed.

He then returned to the living room to sit before the fire and enjoy the cozy warmth of the glowing embers. The motion of the ancestral rocking chair soon started a train of reverie that carried him back some forty years to his boyhood days in Vermont. He recalled the wild adventure, for a boy of twelve, when his father took the family and made the long trip from Guildhall, Vermont to Oberlin by wagon, canal boat, steamboat and stagecoach. Only two years before they arrived, Oberlin had been an unnamed spot in the midst of a forest in the Western Reserve about thirty-five miles from Cleveland.

3

The settling of the wilderness and life in a growing college town were part of a life of action, in startling contrast to the thoughts of retirement which had occupied his mind of late. Raising a family of seven and giving them an education had taxed the physical and financial resources of Heman and Sophronia Hall.

Sounds of activity in the kitchen eventually ceased. Sophronia and her daughter Julia entered the living room and sank into chairs without speaking. Presently Sophronia's head began to nod, but with an effort she kept her eyes open. Her glance fell upon the mantel and she stepped across the room to wind the clock, giving the customary signal for bed. Thus closed the day for the Hall family.

Heman Bassett Hall was graduated from Oberlin in the Class of '47 and followed his academic work with three years' study in Oberlin Theological Seminary. His eyes were not so continuously buried in books at the seminary that they had no time for the young ladies. Long before graduation they focused on attractive Sophronia Brooks, and eyes and heart approved. Heman and Sophronia were married November 6, 1849 at the bride's home, Carlisle, six miles from Oberlin.

Heman had volunteered for service with the American Missionary Association, a powerful Christian antislavery society which was strongly supported by Oberlin men and money. Soon after graduation from the seminary, the handsome young couple sailed for Jamaica Mission in the West Indies. For the next ten years they were busily engaged in promoting the welfare of their freedmen congregation and bringing up the five little Halls who had arrived at fairly regular intervals. Their first-born was a son, George Edward Hall. In time, the Sunday School Roster at Brainerd Station carried these names:

> George Edward Hall—February 23, 1851
> Ellen Julia Hall—November 7, 1852
> Lewis Albert Hall—May 17, 1855
> Emily Brooks Hall—September 13, 1857
> Julia Brainerd Hall—November 11, 1859.

The outbreak of the Civil War forced the American Missionary Association to close its foreign missions. So in 1860 after ten years of service in Jamaica, Heman and Sophronia packed their household belongings and took their little brood to Ohio. Heman's health had been impaired by the hardships of living in Jamaica and Lewis, his second son, died about a year after their return to the States.

The Rev. Mr. Hall's next pastorate was in the forty-year-old Congregational Church of Thompson, Ohio. This little village, nestling in maple shade and flanked by rolling farmland, is about ten miles from the shore of Lake Erie and some thirty-five miles east of Cleveland. The old church was razed years ago, but the unpretentious frame house which served as the parsonage still stands with shuttered windows and vine-covered porch. Here on December 6, 1863, Charles Martin Hall was born.

Recent search in the old church records brought to light several items telling of the pastoral services of Heman and Sophronia Hall:

"Thompson, Ohio, May 4, 1862

The Rev. H. B. Hall commenced his ministerial labors with this church and society May 4, 1862, for the sum of $300.00 and donations, and that amount is secured by the Trustees.

Heman Bassett Hall—Sophronia Brooks Hall—a handsome young couple

April 30, 1863

The annual meeting; the Trustees report they have settled with Rev. H. B. Hall for his services for the year, $300.00 and $100.00 donations, and that within the year there has been contributed $250.00 and the society has expended the same in putting a bell of 503 pounds weight upon the House of Worship.

Sister Sophronia Hall, wife of Rev. Hall, undertook to solicit a subscription from all she met to procure a bell and was successful, and one procured weighing 518 pounds, costing $250.00 and was a fine, silver-toned one, keyed on C.

May 4, 1865

The ministerial labors of the Rev. Mr. H. B. Hall ceased this day, according to contract. Rev. and Mrs. Hall were dismissed by letter to the Church of Christ in Huntsburg.

H. E. Masely, Clerk"

Huntsburg, where the Hall family next moved, was another little Ohio village about ten miles south of Thompson. The stay here only lasted a year. Then the Rev. Mr. Hall's ministerial duties were transferred to Dover where the family settled down for seven years.

While the family was living in Dover, both George and Ellen entered Oberlin College and were necessarily away from home during the school year. During this period, the long college vacation occurred during the winter. Sister Julia, who was four years older than Charles, had reached an age where she could take the responsibility of looking after her little brother and be his playmate. Excursions by stream and through the woods fascinated both children and helped build an understanding and companionship which was to be a vital factor in both their lives.

Charles and his younger
sisters

The pleasures the boy Charles received from trees and flowers, from birds and all the wonders of nature, was repaid with interest by the man Hall in his days of prosperity. Oberlin is grateful to Hall for the beauty he added to the community through his endowment of the Village Improvement Society, providing for the care and development of the college campus and Tappan Square and for the creation of the Hall Arboretum with its collection of representative North American trees.

The intellect-bearing chromosomes of the Hall family were showing their presence in Charles at an early age. His grandfather, Josiah Brewer Hall, was a trustee of Oberlin College in the period 1839-50. Samuel Read Hall, Charles's greatuncle and Josiah's brother, was the first president elect of Oberlin College and earned a national reputation as an educator in New England. To the regret of the Oberlin College authorities, Samuel Read Hall, because of illness, never came west to take up the position of president at Oberlin.

Charlie's education began at home, and with the guidance of his mother, he was able to read much sooner than the neighborhood children of his age. Years later Julia recalled that:

> "My brother used my father's college chemistry as a reader, at an age when bright children do not often know their letters. He would spread the book out on the floor and then lie down on his face to read, with his elbows on the floor, and his head resting on his hands above the open book.

> "I have often seen him, after he had read for a while, lying asleep with his face on the book. He had become tired and was resting as a baby should, for he was only a baby then. Someone would pick him up, still sleeping, and put him and his beloved book in a safe place. But even though so young, he seemed by some marvelous insight to understand what he read."

Charles's interest in books and study was naturally stimulated by the intellectual atmosphere of the Hall household. He browsed among the volumes on his father's bookshelves without restraint. At the age of eight he began attendance at public school in Dover and made rapid progress in his studies. School was almost a formality for this lad who found pleasure in mathematical problems even before he had learned to read. The seed of independent and original thought was being planted in Charles early in life.

As the family grew, educational problems became more pressing, since two little sisters, Edith and Louie, had been added to the list of prospective matriculates of Oberlin College. Viewing the future with some apprehension, the Rev. Mr. Hall resigned his pastorate in Dover when Charles was ten years old and returned to Oberlin.

Just forty years before, the founders had selected the name Oberlin for this community even before a tree had been felled. The name was that of Jean Frederic Oberlin, a famous Lutheran pastor who devoted his life to the material and spiritual welfare of the people in a little village in Alsace.

In the two years between the founding of Oberlin and the arrival of Charles's grandparents, the forest had been cleared for the homes of the early group of settlers, and the first building of Oberlin Collegiate Institute erected, with two more under way. The founders planned Oberlin as a colony consecrated to Christian living, and the college was to be the gathering point in a community devoted to high thinking and plain living.

Innovation moved in with the colonists, who were imbued with a resurgence of the spirit that brought their Pilgrim ancestors to New England. Oberlin College, as the institute was renamed, was the first coeducational college in the United States. The college, after heated argument, decided to admit Negroes. Many of the students and colonists became active abolitionists. Slave-hunters, on occasion, located a traveler on the Underground Railroad, hiding in Oberlin. It was Oberlin's boast, however, that no fugitive slave was ever carried back to bondage, thanks to the wit and courage of the students and colonists. It is understandable that innovations in college and colony were followed by some controversy but they were also accompanied by a surprising degree of tolerance.

In the early days, the theological school at Oberlin was an outstanding department of the college. It eventually became widely known for the "Oberlin Theology," a modified form of Calvinism which included as one of its tenets the doctrine of free will as opposed to determinism. There was a breath of liberalism in their teaching which was characteristic of the pioneers who settled this region. Nevertheless their standards of personal behavior were rigid in many respects. Students at Oberlin pledged themselves not to partake of alcohol or tobacco in any form. In the early days even the drinking of tea was frowned upon, although this attitude was modified in time. The reading of novels was considered time wasted and slightly immoral. However, the publication of *Uncle Tom's* Cabin by Harriet Beecher Stowe in 1852 provided a novel which the reform leaders could approve and the unreasonable attitude toward novel-reading began to moderate.

It was in this college atmosphere that Heman Hall grew to manhood and entered the ministry. Exposed to the same environment, George, his eldest son, followed the paternal pattern except for a finishing touch of three years at Yale Divinity School. With George away at school, Charles grew up in a household largely populated by women,—his mother, two big sisters, two little sisters, and Julia, who was just the right age to understand him.

Charles finished his elementary schooling at such an early age that his parents decided to postpone his high school studies for a year, so that he might study music and the piano. Time proved that Charles had both a gift and a liking for music. He learned to play with a beauty of expression and feeling that charmed his family and made his practicing a pleasure rather than something to be endured. Throughout his life he found in the piano a refuge that brought relaxation from the tensions of living, and even helped clarify his thinking on scientific problems. Charles's love of music and his kinship

11

with nature were inner resources which made him good company for himself when he might otherwise have been a very lonesome person.

The regular three-year course at Oberlin High School and a year at Oberlin Academy comprised Charles's preparation for college. During these years he was also enrolled for part-time work in the Oberlin Conservatory of Music. This was an important period in the education of this young American inventor, for during this period the amorphous interests of the boy began to crystallize into the pattern of the man. These interests—music, applied chemistry and invention—were to last for life.

Charles's insatiable curiosity for knowledge of chemistry was paralleled by the boy's interest in seeing how things worked. Experiments were carried out in the woodshed, in the kitchen, and even in the cupola atop the two-story family residence at 34, later changed to 64, East College Street. The cupola provided a certain intriguing secrecy which matched the mood in which many an experiment was launched. On one occasion during high school days, an experiment in the cupola was too successful, for the succeeding fire brought the family running. However, the blaze was extinguished with only the loss of a tablecloth and a lecture from father on such Mephistophelean activities.

Chemicals from the Hall kitchen shelves provided the ingredients for many an experiment. The addition of vinegar to a solution of washing soda would make it bubble and fizz with carbon dioxide gas. The village pharmacy supplied crystals of blue vitriol, which formed a beautiful blue solution when dissolved in water. A piece of iron dipped into this solution of copper sulfate would plate itself with copper by galvanic action. Alum, dissolved in water, formed a colorless solution, but it became milky with white aluminum hydroxide when a little soda was added. Such experiments as these, which Charles read about in books on chemistry helped fortify his basic knowledge of chemical science. Other ideas for experiments not in the books, helped develop a strain of originality in his thinking. From boyhood it was evident that Charles was more likely to labor in the fields of technology than in theology.

Naturally, Charles's interest in chemistry extended to the element aluminum. In 1892 Charles testified "I have known about aluminum from the time when I first studied chemistry, probably since 1877 or 1878; I was especially struck with the fact that although the most abundant metal in nature—one of the books on chemistry which I studied stating that every clay bank was a mine of aluminum—and exhibiting many of the qualities of the precious metals, it yet, owing to the difficulties of its extraction, was made only in small quantity, and at a cost about equal to that of silver; I was acquainted with the then process of its manufacture, namely, by the reduction of its chlorides by metallic sodium (a purely chemical process); also with its various compounds, as well as with the properties of the metal itself, and knew that the oxide of aluminum was by far the cheapest and most easily prepared pure compound of the metal."

As he grew older his reading and thinking turned more and more to the art of invention. Spending money was scarce in the large Hall family and Charles, as a boy, had mowed lawns in summer, shoveled snow in winter, and done other chores to earn a little cash. Even through his years in college, he found little time for play because of the time devoted to work and study. His dream of becoming prosperous through invention was becoming a driving force.

13

West College Street facing the College Campus in Oberlin in 1878

Oberlin, like many another American town, had a Main Street. Crossing Main Street and marking the southern edge of the campus ran College Street. Looking west from the corner of Main and College, a photograph taken in 1878 showed three frame buildings followed by a series of two- and three-story brick business buildings with the Second Congregational Church near the corner of Professor Street. The third of the frame buildings was Oberlin Hall, the first college building, erected in 1833. Oberlin Hall had lost its academic standing prior to 1860 and had been converted to the service of American enterprise. The first floor housed the village pharmacy, Morris's Meat Market and Barnard's General Store. A sign, "Photograph Gallery," painted on the third floor front proclaimed the location of a photographer who helped pre-

14

serve for posterity the likenesses of Oberlin's faculty, students and townspeople. Neatly ensconced between the pharmacy and Carpenter's Feed Store was a shop labeled "BOOKS" in letters three feet high. These village shops were entrenched behind a row of wooden hitching posts to which a score of farmers' wagons and their equine motive power were anchored during business hours. Across the unpaved street on the campus corner was the village pump and watering trough and behind it Oberlin's famed "Historic Elm." The three frame buildings were removed from the Oberlin Scene by a destructive fire in May of 1886.

Errands for his mother to the Meat Market and General Store provided opportunities for Charles to drop into Edwin Regal's Book Shop and browse among the books with a minimum cash expenditure. The *Scientific American* contained many interesting items on science and invention. From reading about the experiences of other inventors Charles was gradually gaining a knowledge of patent practice which proved invaluable. In this reading he learned about some of the pitfalls which trap the unwary inventor. The value of secrecy in the early development of an invention was so impressed on the lad that secrecy about his schemes became a trait coloring many of his activities, and a trait which was accentuated by his natural shyness.

One inventor, about whom Charles read every bit of information he could find, was often in the news at this time. At the age of twenty-three, this brilliant young man had made what proved in time to be the most important invention of his productive career. The airbrake which he successfully patented was helping spread a network of iron rail across the United States and knitting the nation together with fast transportation. This, and railroad signaling devices which gave

15

vision to the Iron Horse, were making George Westinghouse a wealthy man at the age of thirty. Here indeed was a pattern for any young American inventor.

Charles took his place in the Hall family procession through Oberlin College in the fall of 1880 when he was just a few months short of his seventeenth birthday. Slender of build, he stood about five feet eight inches in height. His brown hair, straight as his New England conscience, was parted slightly to the left of center. In facial feature, there was a marked resemblance to his mother, and his clear blue eyes greeted you with a somewhat shy but friendly look. Charles was decidedly youthful in appearance, a characteristic which he never lost until weakened by his struggle with illness in the last few years of his life.

2

. . . a rich inventor
someday

A HOT JULY SUN beat down upon Charles as he trudged along a dusty Ohio road near Bloomville. His objective was a farmhouse near the top of a slight hill not far away. As he neared the farmyard gate he stopped and leaned against the rail fence. Carefully balancing on the top rail the large book he carried, Charles slowly surveyed the farmyard scene.

A windmill attracted his attention and he gazed idly at the blades barely moving in the feeble breeze. After a minute or so, his interest quickened and he studied the structure intently. Finally he found an old stub of a pencil in his pocket and made a simple sketch on the back of an envelope enclosing his weekly letter from the folks in Oberlin. Then straightening his tie and slicking back his hair, Charles confidently approached the kitchen door.

A woman with her back to the door was standing at the kitchen stove, stirring the contents of an iron kettle. Charles

18

knocked hopefully and ventured a "Good day, Madam." A tired-faced oldish young woman turned and moved slowly to the door. The faint whiff of a savory stew was so diverting that Charles forgot for an instant the object of his visit. The heavy book under his arm reminded him, however, that his board bill of $3.50 was due Saturday and he was short of cash.

"Madam," he said, "I have here a wonderful book. The *Golden Censer* tells you all about the duties of today and the hopes of the future. It will answer your questions about love, courtship and marriage. See where it says—'Man is the creature of interest and ambition—but a woman's whole life is a history of the affections. The heart is her world; it is there ambition strives for empire.' "

His listener sighed a bit, so Charles continued—"In the chapter on Courtship it tells you that—'There is no possible chance of a man being worse off married than single. Sing merrily while you build the nest which will hold the mate in warmth and comfort.' "

There was a distant look on her face as she inwardly contemplated a nest with warmth and comfort, so he continued— "According to government statistics, the married woman is healthier than the maid."

A look of incredulity was spreading over the woman's face when Charles quoted from the chapter on Wedded Life— "Be kind to your wife," says the *Golden Censer*. "If you find this difficult, carry out the resolution as well as you can. You will do better on the second trial."

At this point her stolid face relaxed and she laughed heartily. Charles himself couldn't conceal a boyish grin. Suspecting from his dusty shoes and clothes that he might have had a long and tiring walk, she said, "Won't you have a bit of stew?" Charles responded enthusiastically and while he was enjoying a plateful, his prospect leafed through the pages of the *Golden Censer,* stopping here and there to read a choice bit of advice or to examine the woodcuts illustrating the volume. Finally, closing the book with a snap, she said, "I'm sorry, but I can't buy the book without speaking to my husband," and it was said in such a way that Charles felt a return visit would be hopeless.

Charles, like several other Oberlin College boys, was spending part of his summer vacation following his sophomore year taking subscriptions to the *Golden Censer* and other books. The *Golden Censer* was the kind of book with a fancy, gold-stamped cover kept on the parlor table, and even sometimes read. It offered advice on many problems of everyday living—etiquette, business, love and marriage. The style and content were such, however, that it is questionable whether much of it was taken seriously. One of its principal functions was to show Sunday visitors that the family owned a big book.

When the paths of these college boys crossed, they compared notes on sales and swapped tales. From time to time, Charles gave Julia an account of some of the other Oberliners such as Charles Purple '83, Sidney Haskell '84, Harry Cake '81, Oliver Wells '84, George Waldron '84 whom he met in this way. The best sellers were the Bible and the Revised New Testament. Other agents in other years, however, had just about saturated the market for this best-seller of all time. The *Royal Path* and *Practical Life* were two books, much like the *Golden Censer,* which Charles met in competition. The *Women of Mormonism* attracted curious readers, and people kept asking for a book about the most recent sensation: James Garfield had been shot the year before and Charles Guiteau, his assassin, had just been hanged in June of '82.

20

The letters which Charles wrote his family while he was traveling the countryside selling the *Golden Censer* give interesting glimpses of life at that period. The letters also illustrate the determination and persistence, as well as the sense of humor, which Charles showed in the face of the many discouragements he met in selling unnecessary books to reluctant customers.

Some of the letters, written during that summer vacation, told of ideas for inventions which occurred to Hall as he went from town to town. Charles was beginning to take invention seriously and told Julia to "Keep this letter and all the others. They may be useful in a future lawsuit or something." This and similar requests made later, motivated Julia in preserving so many of her brother's letters.

One of these, written by Charles while working out of Bloomville, about 50 miles from Oberlin, is particularly interesting for the picture it presents of Charles's day-to-day experiences as a book agent.

"Bloomville, Ohio, July 6th, 1882

"Dear Folks,

"At present I am just keeping ahead of my expenses but I am learning fast. When I first started in there was no one except a very foolish old woman whom I could even get to like the book. Today nearly everyone whom I called on (some of them ladies who would compare very favorably with such people as Mrs. Shurtleff and Mrs. Brand at Oberlin) showed very plainly that they thought it a very fine and valuable book, but I couldn't get them to subscribe. One reason is because there have been so many book agents through here lately. I have taken to showing the quotations of poetry in it which are indeed very fine and a few nice parts which I have found in it. Meanwhile there have been

21

several, one who took the book for its good looks, another because he thought it would help him in his business, another took it for the children (and she had plenty) and another sad-faced woman for some reason that I don't know. So altogether in four days I have made four dollars and thirty-five cents and had experiences much more valuable. When I get through here I expect to do much better, as the other towns are not on the direct road and are not canvassed so much. I have gotten clear off the formula I learned.

"I want Father to understand that my courage has not gone out of my boots so that I want to come home and saw wood or pump the washing machines. On the contrary I have quite as good spirits here as anywhere.

"There is a young man here (rich and intelligent) to whom perhaps I could sell our *Britannica,* which is now growing musty in my room. I sold him the *Golden Censer* and he said he wanted to get an encyclopedia, didn't know of the *Britannica,* mentioned *Zell's.* If Eddie has not got one and wants to get one, why he would be the one to take ours if we wanted to dispose of it. I don't think we better keep ours if we can turn it into money. I should not dispose of it for less than six dollars and a half a volume. If you think best write me and I will speak to said boy, and if he wishes will send for a volume and the specimen pages.

"By the way, if any of you hear of or see an advertisement of the life of Guiteau let me know immediately. If I am not doing well at the G.C. I would leave it and take to that. Three people here have even spoken of that, thinking it would sell well and I suppose it would, though I should be careful in the selection of right territory.

"This is the greatest place for subscription Bibles I ever

saw, Bible dictionaries, and histories of the Bible. Quite a number have shown me high-priced copies of the Revised Testament, and in every house almost I see huge illustrated Bibles with paneled covers as big as barn doors. The people with whom I am boarding are not quite as toney as some. They went off to a dance at Republic Tuesday night and danced all night.

"I think that if Jo. ever has to teach again, around here would be a fine place. Younguns are mostly nice appearing and well behaved, and I should judge that good salaries were paid from the looks of things. There are four comparatively large churches here in this small town—Presbyterian, Baptist, M. E. and Reformed Methodist. The last is the largest. The minister of this church was the first man I called on. His wife was the simple woman who took the book and they invited me to dinner.

"Up to today Waldron has taken only one name. He wrote me that he had fished all day without success and was now going to cast the nets on the other side of the ship. He had worked all the time in the town and was going to try the country. Most of the people you meet here say "Howdedo" to you, girls and all, though not always the latter. It seems a little funny.

"I am glad to hear that Alice is better, as I received a postal tonight from home and that other things are as usual. Tell Mother to take a sunbath till it burns if she can get in the right place and get well as soon as possible. I sent a postal this noon saying that I should make a change of territory, but from experiences this afternoon have changed my mind to stay and benefit Seneca County by selling them many *Golden Censers*."

Yours. aff.

C. M. H."

Julia Brainerd Hall, devoted sister and faithful correspondent,
at age of 22

In his letters, Charles went to some length to assure the family that he was getting along all right and to entertain them with his "funny experiences." While canvassing near Findlay, Ohio, he had a couple of "experiences" which he passed on to the family. His telling of the story displays a dry sense of humor and also the ability to laugh at himself when the occasion demanded it.

"Friday I came across one of those 'very too too' girl graduates of the High School of this year I suppose. Well she was talking about a book somewhat like mine *The Royal Path*. She thought it very commonplace. Said that at graduating exercises she had an essay on 'The Flight of Time' or some such topic and when she came to read the chapter in the *Royal Path* on that subject she found it just like her essay. Evidently she gets a great deal of comfort out of the recollection of that greatest of occasions.

"Last night I got into a pretty fix but got out again without serious damage. I went to a nice house—the side door, it was open. There were 8 or 10 females sitting around. A young lady came forward and looked and looked at my book respectfully. One, about 30, began to stare at my shoes which are sadly battered and ragged though I keep them well blacked, and seemed amused at something—the rest kept silence all. Well I got away pretty soon and had a good laugh to myself. I am going to get me some new shoes as soon as I can sell some of the books ordered."

It did not take Charles long to acquire a blasé attitude toward the *Golden Censer*. Although he sold ten copies the first week, eight the second and nineteen the third week of canvassing, he wrote Julia:

"The book I still think is a fraud, on the agents at any rate. A few with a good talent for misrepresenting are selling from 20 and 18 to 32 a week in the territory just adapted to it, like down on the Ohio River at Portsmouth. Still I shall keep at the G.C. till I work out the best portions of Findlay and country around and get something better. If I had something real good, I could make from $10 to $20 a day in good territory and at good time of the year. I saw a copy of that *Practical Life* last night. It is as large a book as that '*100 Great Events*' we have at home. There is 2 or 3 times as much reading in it as in G.C."

After thus discussing the book business situation with Julia, Charles closed this letter with a bit of colorful local gossip.

"I like my boarding place here better than in Bloomville. They had a Dutch blacksmith there. The skunk of a woman thought more of him than of her own husband. Cheated at croquet and cheated me out of a dollar on board, though I had a time with her and gave her less than she demanded. She and her husband had a fight one day."

Charles always showed a tender solicitude for his mother. His letters, aside from bits of news, offered various suggestions for helping her regain her health:

"Tell mother I went to church twice last Sunday and I am going tonight and what is the matter with the young ones, don't they care to write to me.

"I hope Mother is better. Remember that it is primarily a nervous trouble and anything that helps the nerves will help everything and vice versa, company, etc. I think perhaps a galvanic battery would help her, you know that is good for nervousness. I don't mean galvanic but magnetic or induction coil. It seems to me that that electric brush you mentioned must be a fraud as far as electricity is concerned, though it would probably help like any other flesh brush."

Julia was graduated from Oberlin in '81 and soon began to take over the responsibilities of running the home and mothering the family. Their mutual interests established a strong bond between Charles and Julia and, as he grew older, Charles became more and more "the man of the house." On one occasion, in '82, Charles wrote Julia:

"What extra time you have, devote to educating Edie [Edith] and Louie. Get them interested in reading my books of poetry and other good books. By the way, those library books of mine have been returned, I suppose. If not, you needn't pay any fines on them, as my being out of town is excuse enough. But about the children's reading. I presume the children read enough but you must get them to read the right kind. Don't be afraid that it will hurt them. It may come hard at first but if they keep at it they will soon like it. Byron's *Prisoner of Chillon* will be easy to read, also Coleridge's *Rime of the Ancient Mariner,* Wordsworth's *Idiot Boy,* Scott's *Lay of the Last Minstrel* and *Lady of the Lake,* Shakespeare's *Midsummer Night's Dream,* this especially and others which you can pick out. If they can but get a taste for such things, you don't know how much it will help them. Then get them to read that green book in Father's bookcase, *'Science and the Bible,'*—it is real simple and entertaining. It is where I got my first science."

Charles occasionally offered advice on other family problems:

"Have the children [Edie and Louie] tend to those strawberries as I told you as the potatoes are dug. Set them in the little bed in rows 2 feet apart and the plants a foot apart in the row, and pull all the runners off in the large beds. This is necessary if we (are to) have any next year."

During his freshman and sophomore years Charles found little time for college activities. If he had any spare time it was spent in study and work, for there was little spare cash in the Hall household. For Charles and hundreds of other boys and girls, the expense of attending Oberlin College was very modest. The school year was divided into three terms of twelve weeks and the tuition was $3 per term with incidental expenses of $7. There was a special fee of $5 for chemical laboratory supplies and $10 for the course in qualitative analysis. Of course Charles lived at home, just a block from the campus.

The Oberlin College seal bears the motto LEARNING AND LABOR but many of the boys and girls did not take this admonition as literally as did Charles. He took his pleasure in reading along scientific lines with occasional relaxation at the piano. A classmate, Homer Johnson, recalls that "during his days in college we didn't have play enough with him. While he had the gift of humor, he did not have the time or inclination to devote himself to the sports that most of us took time from our studies to engage in. At any rate, with that gift of humor, and that hearty 'Good morning,' bashfully, shyly, even shrinkingly given, he was after all a popular fellow among us."

Charles was interested in everything that went on at Oberlin and was building that loyalty to the college which is characteristic of its host of graduates. One evening after a day's tiring effort of selling the *Golden Censer,* Charles wrote Julia:

> "I rode into town tonight from 6 or 7 miles out with an old Oberlin student, George C. Bright. He was there in '71 and graduated at Cornell in '75. One of the smartest lawyers of Cincinnati, had been all over Europe, makes lots of money now, gave me some reminiscences of Oberlin. He came on at Senior Prep. Ex. in '71, had an oration of the 'English Drama,' said it was the silliest thing he ever saw. He was the one that took down that gorilla from the museum and hung it on the monument, was never found out. A very smart man."

The Affair of the Kidnapped Gorilla had become a legend at Oberlin. Shumway ('82) and Brower ('83) in their little book on Oberliniana have told the story in these words: "Some college boys, resolved that they must do something to break the monotony, proceeded to the College Cabinet, broke down the door and triumphantly bore his apeship away. Hurrying along South Professor Street with their strange prize, it occurred to them that no more conspicuous place for depositing it could be found than on the new Soldier's Monument. Accordingly, one of the boys ran over into the Ladies' Hall premises and purloined a nightshirt from the clothesline. With this and some other articles of clothing, they rigged up the poor gorilla artistically. Then they fastened a rope about his neck and elevated him by means of the derrick until he was ignominiously suspended over the monument about twenty feet from the ground. There he was left until morning. Some early risers made the discovery and rushed to the spot, greatly horrified to think that a lynching had been perpetrated within the borders of consecrated Oberlin. The truth was speedily comprehended and the gorilla promptly returned to the museum." The exposure and rough treatment did not improve the gorilla's general disposition but he became one of Oberlin's best-known characters.

Charles always recalled these stories of college pranks with a kind of vicarious pleasure for he was just a college boy at heart. He could picture vividly the consternation of the bell ringer on the morning the Chapel bell failed to ring after some student had removed the clapper. He thought the scheme of tearing up the dilapidated plank walk across the campus a good one; then the college authorities just *had* to repair it.

In his letters to Julia, Charles made mention from time to time of inventions which were churning around in his mind. His sister, in an excess of caution, occasionally crossed out names and phrases in these letters, as in the following:

"I had a letter from XXXXXXXX last night. He is going to do all he can about that smoke invention of mine, though not until we find that it is new and our invention by consulting the *Scientific American*. He thinks it is a good idea, but will take a good deal of experimenting to develop (I don't agree with that).

"Well, about that subject we are most interested in. I won't go at length to describe it as you know of it already, except that I will say that the difficulties (and I don't think there are many) can be overcome by a little inventive ingenuity. Uncle George is the man to help me put it through. He has plenty of money idle and is interested in inventions."

Sister Julia wrote on the back of the envelope, "This letter shows what was always true of him—that he never saw a piece of machinery that didn't set him to thinking of possible improvement."

By July 27, the idea that struck Charles as he was watching the farmer's windmill had crystallized and he put it down on paper with sketches, in writing his sister Julia from the town of Findlay:

"Now here is something else which struck me on that day, Thursday, the 7th of July, as I was watching a windmill. (They have lots of those things in this country.) And that is to improve the thing by putting around or rather in front of the vanes, a funnel sort of thing of light sheet metal to concentrate the breeze. You know the energy of the wind is something like this, at 2 miles an hour it would not stir the mill, at 4 perhaps a little, at 8 four times as strongly as at 4, at 16 four times as strongly as at 8 and so as the square of the velocity. And then it seems to me cheaper to have the wheel 4 feet in diameter and a funnel of light cheap sheet metal to cover the rest of 6 or 8 feet, than to have a wheel simply 8 feet in diameter, and then the wheel with a funnel could use a wind that the wheel alone could not. I think you get my idea. Maybe it would be an improvement and maybe it is not.

"Yes, I really think I shall be a rich inventor some day.
Yours aff.

C. M. Hall"

Charles's scheme of leading the wind to the vanes of a windmill through a funnel-shaped guide was ingenious even though he overlooked aerodynamic factors which defeated the purpose of the contraption. The *Golden Censer* told Charles that he lived in a land "where the genius of the inventor has exceeded with its results the wonders of the Arabian Nights." Although Charles's idea for a superefficient windmill was not exactly a stroke of genius, it strengthened his confidence in his budding inventiveness.

3

*. . . he would lay up a
great fortune*

JUNIOR YEAR was the high point in Charles's college course. This was the time to which he had been looking forward. He could now enjoy two terms of chemistry with lectures by Professor Jewett, and work in a real chemical laboratory under his supervision. Although instruction in chemistry was given in a dilapidated old brick building converted for the purpose, that fact took away none of the glamour which it held in Charles's eyes. Cabinet Hall, for so the building was named, housed in the north wing of the first floor a lecture room, a large chemical laboratory, a small private laboratory, a stock room and an office for Professor Jewett. In winter, heat was supplied by coal-burning stoves which attempted, but with little success, to warm the chilling breezes which swept through cracks and crevices in walls and flooring. On the third floor was the cabinet of natural history, the home base of the college gorilla.

34

Charles was fortunate to have such a scholar as Frank Fanning Jewett as his teacher of chemistry. Jewett had the finest of training with degrees from Yale, a year's study in Germany and a year's experience assisting Wolcott Gibbs at Harvard University. Then followed four years (1876-1800) as Professor of Chemistry in the Imperial University of Tokyo in Japan.

Although slender and a little under average in height, his scholarly appearance commanded attention. Piercing blue eyes, deep set under shaggy eyebrows, could twinkle on occasion. He gave his best to the interested student and expected the student's best effort in return.

Charles first met Professor Jewett soon after he took up his professional duties at Oberlin in the fall of 1880. He came to the laboratory to buy a few cents' worth of glass tubing and test tubes for some of his home experiments. He came again after a while to get some more things to work with. This earnest youth interested Professor Jewett and he chatted with him occasionally during these visits. He didn't learn much about Charles's experiments, for the boy was rather noncommunicative. Charles did, however, confide the fact to Professor Jewett that he was speculating on possible ways of producing aluminum from its ores.

Charles's promise as a schoolboy was maintained in college. Professor Jewett said that "he studied chemistry in the regular classes, understood thoroughly the lessons assigned, and carried on his laboratory experiments with intelligent insight. He always knew what he was doing and what the experiments were intended to teach. Moreover, he was constantly busy, never idle." There is also evidence that he occasionally undertook experiments not in the text book.

One wintry morning in the second term, Charles hurried

35

Frank Fanning Jewett—Professor of Chemistry at Oberlin College

across the campus to Cabinet Hall. He didn't want to miss a word of Professor Jewett's lecture for he knew what the subject was to be. Professor Jewett entered the room with a cheery "Good morning, gentlemen" and advanced to his lecture table. After adjusting his eyeglasses, arranging his notes and calling the class roll, he proceeded with the day's lecture in a crisp, precise manner:

"Today, I am going to tell you about aluminum. But, first, a little story of how I first met this wonderful metal.

"During the years 1874 and '75, I studied chemistry at the University of Goettingen in Germany. Occasionally, there would appear in the chemical laboratory a very old man with a long, deeply wrinkled face, with stooping shoulders and a shuffling walk. He usually wore a rather long coat and a large German cap with a good-sized visor. He passed around among the students, and once in a while would stop and talk with me about my work. This man was Friedrich Wöhler, one of the great German chemists of his day. Wöhler it was who discovered the element aluminum in 1827 and through him I first became acquainted with this beautiful metal.

"I am holding up a small piece of aluminum for you to see. I bought this while I was in Germany, for aluminum is not yet made in America.

"In 1845, Wöhler was able to make a few small beads of aluminum by a chemical reaction between aluminum chloride and potassium metal. From weighing these small pieces, he learned that aluminum was a very light metal.

"By the year 1854, Henri Sainte-Clair Deville, working in Paris had developed a much better method using the metal sodium to free the aluminum from aluminum chloride. Through Sainte-Clair Deville's work, the first bars of aluminum were made and exhibited at the Paris Exposition in 1855. By 1856, he had been able to produce the metal in substantial quantity and to lower the price from $90 to $20 per pound.

"It looks now as if there will be a brilliant future for this light, bright and nontarnishing metal if only some cheap method of production can be found. Aluminum compounds are plentiful—as Sainte-Clair Deville said—'every claybank is a mine of aluminum' but the cost of the sodium and the cost of the aluminum chloride is too high. Even today, aluminum sells for about $15 a pound.

"How many in this class have ever seen a piece of aluminum?"

And only Charles raised his hand, for Professor Jewett had

37

shown him the same piece during a previous conversation. Professor Jewett continued:

"Aluminum is silvery in appearance but does not tarnish like silver. It is light in weight, but strong and is a good conductor of electricity and heat. In the future, hundreds of uses will be found for aluminum."

After some further discussion of the metal and the chemistry of its compounds, Professor Jewett finished his lecture with the prediction:

"If anyone should invent a process by which aluminum could be made on a commercial scale, not only would he be a benefactor to the world but would also be able to lay up for himself a great fortune!"

And Charles turned to a classmate and whispered, "I'll be that man."

Charles's interest in finding a cheap method of producing aluminum had already reached the experimental stage in 1881. Hall testified in 1892 that "at different times for a number of years I experimented with different methods or attempts to produce aluminum cheaply. First in 1881 and in 1883 and 1884."

In his first effort, he attempted to separate aluminum from clay (aluminum silicate) by heating with carbon. Smelting with carbon was the common method for producing iron from its oxide, and while it had been tried before with alumina, Charles thought perhaps the temperature had not been high enough. He ground together some clay and carbon and tried to fuse the mixture by contact with burning charcoal and potassium chlorate. Fortunately, no explosion resulted from the ignition of the charcoal-chlorate mixture but neither did he recover any aluminum.

Charles next tried to improve the current chemical method

of making aluminum by finding a cheaper method of securing the essential aluminum chloride. He heated calcium chloride and magnesium chloride with clay in the hope that aluminum chloride would distill off and be condensed, but without success.

There is a minor mystery in the chronology of Hall's college curriculum which is somewhat puzzling to the historian. The college records show that he registered as a freshman in September 1880 and in the ordinary course of events would have graduated with the class of '84. However, Charles graduated with the class of '85. A study of the annual college catalogues shows that he was registered as a freshman in the college year of 1880-81, a sophomore in 1881-82; a junior in 1882-83 and a senior in 1884-85. His name does not appear in the catalogue for 1883-84. No information seems to be available as to why he absented himself during the 1883-84 year. There is some evidence, however, that he spent an unusual amount of time in experimenting at home during the year 1884. At that time the school year comprised three terms commencing on or about September 14th, January 24th, and April 5th respectively; the third term ended with Commencement at the end of June.

In 1884, he set up a homemade furnace and bellows in a small shed (not the famous woodshed) in the yard back of the Hall home on East College Street. This was a coal-fired contraption arranged like a blacksmith's forge and, with the proper effort on the bellows, a fairly high temperature could be reached. During the summer he tried to reduce pure alumina with carbon but without success even though he reached temperatures capable of fusing platinum. Charles spent a number of weeks at this and other experiments trying to find some catalytic agent which would make it possible to reduce

39

alumina with carbon at a high temperature. Telling of this work, he said "I tried mixtures of alumina and carbon with barium salts, with cryolite, and with carbonate of sodium, hoping to get a double reaction by which the final result would be aluminum.

"I remember buying some metallic sodium and trying to reduce cryolite, but obtained very poor results. I made some aluminum sulphide but found it very unpromising as a source of aluminum then as it has been ever since."

Having run out of ideas, for the moment, on new processes of making aluminum, Charles decided to find new copper alloys which might be good enough to patent and, if he was fortunate, find a buyer for the patent. He spent some time melting copper in his "blast" furnace and alloying it with other metals. He made a record of the most promising alloys by writing a tentative patent application which he duly signed and had witnessed on November 8, 1884. Charles claimed the discovery of new copper alloys containing boron with iron and nickel or manganese. In place of the boron, he found that silicon or titanium might be used; the addition of aluminum was also included. Some of the alloys he mentioned are similar to the modern manganese or silicon bronzes, but his use of boron has not been found advantageous. He concluded from his work that he had produced an alloy with greatly superior corrosion resistance. Charles had only primitive means of testing his alloys and nothing came of this metallurgical effort.

It is evident that Charles had spent some time at the library, studying the form in which patent applications should be prepared so that he might be his own patent agent. Both the bronze alloy just described and an idea for an electric battery were recorded in the form of patent applications which were written on legal paper and signed and witnessed by his sister Julia and his father.

Charles's electric battery project was one on which he worked for years. One of the common experiments of chemistry is to pass an electric current through an electrolyte such as a dilute solution of sulphuric acid and have hydrogen and oxygen liberated at the two electrodes, cathode and anode, in the same proportion in which they occur in the water of the electrolyte. Chemists had speculated on the possibility of developing a cell in which this reaction would be reversed. A gaseous fuel such as hydrogen would be supplied continuously at the surface of the anode and oxygen at the cathode in the presence of a suitable electrolyte with the hope that an electric current would be generated. Such a battery is a possibility if only the practical problems of securing satisfactory electrodes and electrolyte are solved.

Charles stated in his tentative patent application (1884) that "the feature in my battery for which I claim originality is the method of supplying gas to the surface of the plates. I make the plates hollow and of porous carbon, so that the gases may be forced into the interior of the plates whence they may penetrate out through the pores and appear on the outside as fast as they may be consumed." In a second specification which Charles wrote and signed on the same date, he set forth the idea of making the electrode plates or tubes of porous metal and he outlined several schemes for making porous metal tubes.

At this stage of his career, he did not have the tools and materials for working on this new type of electric battery or fuel cell, as it came to be called. Schemes for making such a cell kept running through his mind, however, and from time to time he jotted them down in his notebook. Some years later,

41

when he had money and a workshop in which to try out some of these ideas, he took up the battery project again. The battery was a challenge to which he kept responding with stubborn determination.

During his senior year at Oberlin College, Charles suggested to Professor Jewett that they engage as partners in a search to find a new and better filament material than the carbon fiber which Edison used in the incandescent electric lamp he had invented a few years before. The idea appealed to Professor Jewett and he gave Charles a desk in his private laboratory. A search of the chemical literature gave Charles the idea that tungsten was a refractory metal which might well serve for this purpose. He experimented with tungsten compounds for a season and finally found a material which he thought would make a good filament. Charles left a brief account of this work in a letter to his brother George:

> "I worked some time in making filaments. The first were too large. I made some smaller ones, but the material could not be made in coherent enough form. My fine filaments came apart after heating a minute, whether heated very hot or not. They could be made coherent with suitable apparatus. Some of these filaments of this new material no longer than this —— I made to give an unbearable brilliant light while they lasted."

But his filaments didn't show much promise, and so he turned again to his perennial project. As he told his brother, "Whenever I get temporarily stuck on any other process, I go to work on a cheap process for aluminum."

The failure of the thermal reduction experiments turned Charles's mind to the use of electricity as a more potent agent for the reduction of aluminum from its compounds. Several compounds were considered by Charles and Jewett and they finally decided to try aluminum fluoride. Charles spent many days in treating alumina with hydrofluoric acid in lead dishes and finally decided that he had aluminum fluoride of satisfactory purity. This material was mixed with water and then all the batteries they could find in the laboratory were assembled and a strong current of electricity passed through the mixture. The experimenters could find no aluminum, so they reasoned that perhaps the current was not strong enough and so as Professor Jewett explained, "This battery was then enlarged by additional cells made out of beakers, tumblers, jars and everything else that ingenuity could devise. All to no purpose, however." All they found for their work was a deposit of white aluminum hydroxide on the negative electrode.

Few people in America had seen or handled aluminum in the early '80's. It was a rare metal. Only a few chemists and metallurgists had any familiarity with its properties. Although about 5000 pounds of aluminum had been produced in France in the year 1884, the production in America was only 125 pounds. This metal was made by William Frishmuth in Philadelphia.

In the year 1884, aluminum broke into print in the United States when a public announcement of the Frishmuth process was printed in the *New York Times* for November 25. The announcement made optimistic claims for the ultimate production of cheaper aluminum, and contained an interesting account of the chemical process by which Frishmuth was making aluminum. Included also was a summary of the properties and the uses of this light metal. The article closed with an invitation: "At present anyone in New York or vicinity wishing to see a specimen of the product can do so by visiting Tiffany's where the apex of the Washington Monument at the National Capital, manufactured by order of the Government, is now on exhibition."

The *Cleveland Leader* for Monday morning, December 8, 1884, brought the news to Oberlin that the aluminum cap had finally been set on top of the Washington Monument. The ceremony took place on the birthday of Charles Martin Hall, but, of course, no one yet had reason for noticing any coincidence between those two dates. The *Cleveland Leader* reported the event in the following manner:

Special Correspondence of the *Leader*

Washington, December 6. "Today the aluminum cap was placed on the top of the Washington Monument and its exterior is completed. Five hundred and fifty-five feet high, it has an area at the base large enough for two big city houses, but its top, as it kisses the clouds, is no larger than the point of a pin. At 500 feet above the ground it has four sides each of which is thirty-five feet wide. Its area at this point is that of a comfortable six room house, each room of which might be twelve by sixteen. It would take more than a hundred and twenty-five yards of carpet to cover its floor, and a man with a good elevator might make a pleasant summer residence of a house built up here. This square forms the base of the pyramidal top which runs from it fifty-five feet until it terminates in its metallic point. This point is constructed of the largest piece of aluminum ever made. It is a pyramid nine inches high, which shines like a speck of light away up there under the rays of the sun. It weighs just one hundred ounces and is one-third as light as it would be if it was made of copper. Aluminum does not corrode, and it makes one of the best conductors of lightning. A wire will be fastened to the lower side of this little pyramid and run down into the earth. This will make the longest lightning rod ever constructed."

While the Jewett-Hall partnership was not a financial success and never paid dividends, its returns were in other directions. Having his own desk in a private laboratory amounted to a postgraduate course in research for Charles. Even the negative results of some of the experiments provided clues which were to prove valuable in the future.

Of course there were extracurricular activities of which Charles was not entirely oblivious. Romance on this first coed campus was inevitable even though it received little encouragement from the college authorities according to the reminiscences of old students like Shumway and Brower. Uncharted strolls in the moonlight were forbidden. Student couples took advantage of the walk from choir practice to Ladies' Hall for companionship and conversation on subjects of personal interest. Unfortunately, the walk was only a block long and at the ordinary pace consumed only a few minutes. However, by an evolutionary process, there developed what became known as the "Oberlin Step," which was so gradual and imperceptible that the forward movement seemed little more than that of the growing grass. In this rather inhibited atmosphere, the romance between Heman and Sophronia Hall had blossomed as had many another marriage between Oberlin students.

Most of these restrictions had vanished by the time Charles entered College. He was usually so absorbed in his studies, however, that his growing interest in a classmate named Josephine Cody did not fail to attract the attention of some of his friends. There was speculation as to whether science or this vivacious young beauty was to become the paramount interest in Charles's life. The pair found mutual interests in music and

45

Sunday School but Charles's affectional development was cramped by his drive to become a rich inventor. There is evidence that Charles found it difficult to give expression to the tender sentiment which might have cemented their attraction for each other. Perhaps cautious Charles was waiting for his ship to come in before committing his heart and hand irrevocably.

Charles took a more active part in college activities during his senior year. He was, of course, known to all his classmates and they made him class treasurer. When the time for graduation approached he was put on the committee for arrangements, and when the commencement program was finally arranged he had an oratorical duty to perform. Even though he disliked public speaking, the subject was one which was close to his heart and demanded careful preparation.

Oberlin's fifty-second Annual Commencement Day finally arrived, July 1, 1885. The ceremonies were held in the First Congregational Church which is almost as old as Oberlin itself since its construction was started in 1842. Even today it attracts attention—a simple red brick structure, but beautiful with graceful lines and harmonious proportions. No Very-Important-Person had been imported to tell the graduating class about Life after College, but interspersed among the musical selections by chorus, quartet and trio were numerous orations by the graduates themselves. Scanning the program, Charles found the number which concerned him most:

Science and the Imagination

Charles M. Hall, Oberlin

From time to time during the ceremonies, Charles's gaze rested upon Josephine; but reluctantly each time, he brought his attention back to the program. Time enough for dreaming

46

when his own oration had been delivered and the applause had died away. No copy of Charles's essay is extant but from his life and works, one can imagine what he would say:

First of all a tribute to science and the wonderful understanding of nature it was bringing through discoveries in the fields of botany, geology, physics and chemistry. Then an acknowledgment of the conveniences—yes, the necessities of life—which the inventor through applied science was creating for the service of mankind. With due obeisance to a dozen terms of rhetoric, he might have paused to inform his audience that science was the search for truth or systematized knowledge tested by experiment. Being a student of literature he probably added a few quotations from Shakespeare and his favorite poets.

The "imagination" of Charles's theme was the play of an educated mind which could travel beyond the covers of a textbook in search of new information, new ideas and new theories to explain the behavior of the world around us. He would decry the philosophy of the wishful thinker, that thinking makes it so, and extol the scientist who tests the fruit of his imagination in the laboratory. No doubt in composing his essay, he frequently thought of his secret ambition to bring cheap aluminum to a metal-hungry world; but that was a field he was holding for his own exploration and he wanted no interlopers.

At last, the ceremonies ended, the diplomas were handed to the graduates and he became:

CHARLES MARTIN HALL, A.B., Class of 1885

~∽ *4* ∾~

. . . *in the Immortal*
Woodshed

GRADUATION found Hall without working plans for conquering the world. He had dreamed of becoming a great inventor and a rich one, but none of the schemes which he had conceived had developed into a profit-making project. He was faced like most graduates with the problem of making a living. During a visit to Boston no progress was made, and by summer's end, Hall was home again in the red brick house on East College Street.

His mind had been active, however, during this period. Consciously and subconsciously, he was still working on the problem of producing cheap aluminum. Obviously, the solution of the problem required the formulation of a new strategy, and any plan would require more laboratory space and equipment than he had so far improvised at home.

Fortunately, the woodshed was a fairly large room and it was not difficult to persuade Julia to let him enlarge his working space. Washing machine, sawbuck and woodpile only had to be moved back a bit. Most of the woodshed floor was at kitchen level, but at one side, several steps led to a strip at a lower level. This two-level construction of the woodshed made it convenient for Hall to stand on the lower floor while the edge of the upper floor served as a laboratory table on which he could set supplies and equipment with which he was work- ing. Materials and equipment which would have been in the way on Mondays and other times when the woodshed was also being employed for domestic operations, were stored on shelves along the woodshed walls.

Julia's headquarters were in the adjoining kitchen and she had formed the habit of looking in from time to time to see what her brother was doing in his woodshed laboratory. Her visits were welcomed for she was a good adviser on both personal and scientific problems. She had taken the classical and scientific course at Oberlin, and her training in chemistry enabled her to understand and discuss chemical problems with Charles. Even though she had little of her brother's chemical insight, she was a patient listener and interested questioner.

There was a touch of autumn in the air on the first of October in '85. In the evening after the dishes were washed and the kitchen put to rights, Julia poked her head into the woodshed to see what Charles was doing, and found him busily engaged in making an electrode-holder for a battery. "I don't think," he said, "that it is any use trying to reduce aluminum oxide chemically. Every reaction I tried at the college failed. It looks as though electrolysis would be my only hope. I don't know just how I'll start but anyhow, I'll need some more bat- teries and I might as well get them ready." "Well, don't stay up too late, Charlie," she said as she retreated through the kitchen door bound for bed.

Wearied by the day's activities, Julia fell asleep almost as soon as her head touched the pillow. Toward midnight, she imagined she was dreaming, but it was only the sound of music from the ancient piano in the Hall parlor which was penetrating her consciousness. Soon, half awake, she recognized the second movement of Beethoven's "Appassionata." The music seemed to be interpreting the pianist's mood and slowly she realized that Charles had taken his problem to the piano. The music swept forward as if following the progress of his thinking until the final emphatic bars suggested that at least a clue had been found. In a few seconds, the quiet strains of another melody were heard. The tempo gradually quickened and a note of excitement found its way into the player's touch and music. The excitement grew in urgency as the theme of the "Moonlight Sonata" developed until the crescendo of the final dramatic chords. Utter silence followed and Julia slowly drifted back to sleep.

The next morning, Julia appeared in the kitchen at her usual hour, only to find Charles already at work in the woodshed. "Good morning, Charlie, why were you up so late? It must have been past midnight when I heard you at the piano."

"You know, sis, I've got a new idea for making aluminum. I think I know now why I didn't get any aluminum when Professor Jewett and I put aluminum fluoride in water and tried to separate the metal with an electric battery."

"Do you mean by electroplating it on an electrode?"

"Yes, that was the general idea, but I didn't get any aluminum on the cathode where it should have been. Professor Jewett suggested I try more current; even that didn't work."

Julia thought a moment and then said, "What became of the aluminum?"

"I think," said Charles, "that if I made any aluminum, it

reacted with the water. It may be impossible to electrolyze aluminum from any liquid containing water. I'll have to make a fluid solution of some aluminum compound without water."

"Can't you find that kind of solution in your chemistry books?" asked Julia.

"I've looked," was the reply, "but the subject isn't mentioned. I think the best compound to try to dissolve would be alumina because it is a cheap compound of aluminum. I'm going to start looking for a molten solvent as soon as I can get a good hot furnace. A molten solvent wouldn't hold any water, it would evaporate."

"Why do you need such a hot furnace?"

"Well, I think I'll try and melt some fluorspar and I know it's hard to melt. I'm not even sure that I can make a furnace that will do it."

Charles first considered using the coal-fired furnace and bellows he had built in the small shed back of the woodshed. After some contemplation, however, he abandoned this idea. The furnace was poorly adapted for the electrolytic experiments he planned and the old shed was going to be a mighty cold place in which to work during the coming winter. A gasoline burner heating the inside of an insulated muffle looked like a promising setup and he set out to find a secondhand stove within reach of his emaciated pocketbook.

Weeks passed before Charles secured a single-burner gasoline stove that seemed to meet his requirements. Then he fashioned around the burner a cylindrical iron shell, and lined it with fire clay to hold the heat and withstand the high temperatures anticipated. In the center of this shell and above the burner, he placed the fire-clay crucible in which he was to melt the solvent—if he could find one. Making this furnace took weeks but at last it was ready.

Sophronia Brooks Hall, Charles's mother

The first substance Hall tried as a possible solvent for alumina was calcium fluoride—the common mineral fluorspar. He did not know, however, that this mineral must be heated over 2500°F before it melts. The melting point of fluorspar was beyond the reach of his furnace no matter how hard he "pushed" the flame or how carefully he covered the crucible.

For his next experiment, he decided to try some magnesium fluoride. This compound he had to make, and Professor Jewett let him work in the laboratory using their dishes, oven and other equipment to react magnesia with hydrofluoric acid and dry the product. This material was also a disappointment. It wouldn't melt.

Sodium fluoride and potassium fluoride were the next compounds Charles made. These melted in his gasoline burner furnace but they gave no indication of dissolving alumina. Aluminum fluoride was another compound he made, but it wouldn't melt. Making and trying those compounds was a tedious job and the results up to this point quite discouraging.

What led Hall to choose fluorides for the start of this search is not known. Perhaps it was his college experience with aluminum fluoride that ended in failure. Perhaps he just had an appointment with destiny, for the next compound he tried was the double fluoride, sodium aluminum fluoride, known as the mineral cryolite. The cryolite in his crucible melted eventually to a red-hot, limpid fluid, and when Hall dropped pinches of alumina into the melt, the alumina readily dissolved. This was the morning of Wednesday, February 10, 1886.

On impulse, Charles called Julia to tell her the wonderful news: "Julia, Julia, I'm out in the shed. I've found it at last." Julia dropped her work, rushed through the kitchen and into the woodshed, to find Hall with the glow from the red-hot crucible lighting up his face. "See, sis," he explained, "when I drop a little alumina into this molten cryolite, it dissolves." And Julia saw the white powder gradually disappear in the red-hot fluid which he was stirring with a carbon rod in the crucible. "And look," he exclaimed, "nothing settles out when I stop stirring. The alumina dissolves in molten cryolite just like sugar in water."

"Now, I only have to pass electricity through this solution and I'll get aluminum. I'll need another battery. Maybe I can borrow one from Professor Jewett. You can help me make more alumina, wash and dry it. Then we'll try that big experiment."

Charles had a busy week end. He borrowed a battery from Professor Jewett to make sure of enough current. More alumina had to be precipitated from a solution of alum, and heated red hot to drive out the moisture. Carbon rods for electrodes were already on hand, but Charles had to rig up a stand for holding them in position in the crucible. Julia helped where she could, and everything was ready for the crucial test on Tuesday, February 16.

After melting the cryolite and watching some alumina dissolve, Charles turned on the current. Both watched the red-hot fluid anxiously. "See, Julia, the little bubbles of gas rising around the stick of carbon? That means the electric current is working. It's decomposing something. Let's hope that's aluminum collecting on the other electrode."

They couldn't see anything on the electrode, nor was there anything visible on the bottom of the crucible. After watching for a long time, Charles shut off the current, lifted the electrodes, and poured the molten cryolite into his mother's old iron skillet; there it quickly froze to a white, rocklike material. When it cooled, he broke it up into small lumps but they could find no trace of aluminum. "Oh, Charlie, what shall we do?" And Charles, still hoping, pointed to a white coating on the end of the negative electrode: "That looks like aluminum to me."

Each day, for several days, he repeated the experiment, but still got no aluminum he could collect or handle. In thinking it over, he said to himself, "The cryolite must be dissolving silica from the clay crucible and the electric current is using its strength in separating silicon. Now, if I only had a carbon crucible, this wouldn't happen."

So he made himself a small carbon crucible about two inches wide inside and four inches deep and enclosed it in a tightly fitting clay crucible. By Tuesday, February 23, everything was ready for this next test. Julia had followed all these preparations with great interest, and was on hand to watch when Charles melted the cryolite and alumina in his carbon crucible and connected the electrodes to his battery. As before, the bubbles of gas rising around the carbon anode showed that the electric current was at work. The current was kept on for a long time, to produce as much aluminum as possible. Finally Charles and Julia could contain their curiosity no longer. Charles poured the red-hot liquid into the old skillet and let it cool. As soon as it was cool enough to handle, Charles seized a hammer and broke up the frozen cryolite. Almost at once he spied among the pieces of cryolite, a small silvery button. "I've got it, I've got it," he cried. Julia was so excited she took the hammer and, after a few more whacks, found another silvery button among the broken bits of cryolite. "Oh, Charlie," she said, "it IS aluminum."

And it was aluminum. The little buttons were light to handle and malleable when Charles tapped one with a hammer. That very afternoon he rushed over to Professor Jewett to proudly display his aluminum. Jewett was quite excited over the bright little button and assured Charles that it *was* aluminum.

Amidst the general jubilation of the Hall family, Charles thought many times how happy his mother would have been to have shared in the pleasure of his achievement. But his mother, after several years of illness had died on May 7, 1885. Charles had loved her tenderly and done what he could to lighten her burdens and make her days more comfortable. There was a rare understanding between them.

His brother George was preaching in Dover, New Hampshire, but still took a helpful and, occasionally, a material interest in his little brother's affairs. Just recently he had sent Charles a five- then a ten-dollar bill to help purchase chemicals and supplies for his experiments.

Charles's oldest sister, Ellen, whom he fondly admired, had been graduated from Oberlin, acquired an M.D. degree and married a fellow doctor, George E. Kinsey. They had gone abroad and Ellen's sudden death in Vienna in 1882 brought sorrow which was long in fading from Charles's memory. Sister Emily had married Martin Luther Stimson who took her to China as a missionary in 1882.

This left Julia, Charles, Edith, Louie and their father in the red brick home on East College Street. Edith could no longer be called a little girl for she was now a freshman in Oberlin. The two younger sisters and their father came down to the woodshed to see what the excitement was all about and to be indoctrinated in the Hall process for producing aluminum. For all of them it was a day never to be forgotten. In fact it was a day which would be carefully recorded in the history of invention.

That night Julia agreed with Charles: "I must have some way of proving that I made aluminum today. I'm going to write George a letter and ask him to keep it as a record." "Oh, I know another way of remembering this date," said Julia. "This is George's birthday." And so Charles wrote his brother George a long letter telling of the day's achievement. Julia read the letter, saw Charles sign it, seal it, and address the envelope to the Rev. George E. Hall at Dover, New Hampshire.

The red brick house still stands in Oberlin but Charles's homemade laboratory has vanished from the scene. In the history of invention it has become The Immortal Woodshed.

5

. . . negotiations came
to naught

THE DAY AFTER the great invention found Charles again working intently in the woodshed laboratory. Julia, seeing him, called from the kitchen, "What are you going to do today, Charles?"

"I'm going to try a longer run and make more aluminum than I did yesterday. And then I have an idea for a different kind of positive pole that won't burn up like carbon does. I think also that I'll try adding some sodium fluoride to my electrolyte. Then I'm going to write George again and give him a full account of my process. It will make a good record when I go to the Patent Office."

"Well," said Julia, "call me if you want any help."

Charles had already started the gasoline burner heating his furnace and was drying some alumina for the day's run. This he added to the cryolite saved from yesterday's operation and tamped it into the carbon crucible. He decided there wouldn't be enough electrolyte after it had melted so he added a little more cryolite, carefully covered it with a lid, and lowered the crucible into the furnace. After about an hour's heating the electrolyte had melted sufficiently so that he could put the two carbon electrodes in place and turn on the current. He covered the furnace with a lid which let the electrodes come through but was still tight enough to help keep the heat in. Charles had little to do now except let the electric current make aluminum from the alumina dissolved in the cryolite. He planned to keep the current going most of the day for he wanted to make as much aluminum as possible with the batteries available. While waiting he pondered on the possibility of finding a material for the positive electrode (anode) which would not melt, would not dissolve in the electrolyte and would not contaminate the electrolyte.

Late in the afternoon Charles shut off the current, poured the electrolyte and aluminum into the old iron skillet where it quickly froze to a snow-white mass. When it was cool enough, he called Julia to see what the day's run had brought. Breaking up the frozen mass with a hammer, they proceeded to pick out the globules of aluminum and found quite a harvest. Charles gave Julia several good-sized globules of aluminum as souvenirs of the occasion and these she put in her work basket along with the mending and sewing. She kept them carefully for many years and two of them are now framed and hang proudly on the walls of Alcoa's Aluminum Research Laboratories.

That evening Charles went to his father's desk and wrote a long letter to George. The surprising thing shown by this letter is that Charles had such a broad and clear concept of his invention even before the alumina and cryolite dust had completely settled in the woodshed laboratory.

February 24, 1886

"Dear Brother George:

"I sent you a letter last evening which you will probably receive before this. You may want to know more about the matter of which I wrote, and I will try and enlighten you further. You may ask how I know that enough aluminum can be made by this process to pay for the electricity used. If you will read the article 'Electrolysis' in the 'Ency,' you will find that a definite quantity of electricity, if it will decompose a salt or solution at all, will produce always a definite quantity of metal. There is a table of 'electrochemical equivalents, page 112, Vol. VIII. The same quantity of electricity which will precipitate 31.6 parts of copper or 12 parts of magnesium will precipitate 9.1 parts of aluminum.

"There are other things to be considered, and the chief one is the resistance of the melted salt. I have tried some experiments on that, and as far as I can judge it seems to be very low. If so, that means that a large quantity of metal can be made in a short time with economy of electricity. But if the resistance is not as low as that of some salts, it can be made lower by mixing in the melted compound of other salts, such as chloride of sodium, or potassium, barium, & c., or fluorides of the same metal, none of which will at all affect the operation otherwise than by reducing the resistance of the salt if it is not at the lowest alone.

"There is another thing about this. One of the carbon poles, the positive pole, in the melted mixture will be constantly eaten away and oxidized by the oxygen from the alumina. I know that from theory, and the experiments prove the same thing. If the carbon burned to carbonic oxide CO, two pounds of carbon will be required for three of Al, but if to carbonic acid CO_2 one pound to three of aluminum. You may think this is a disadvantage, but it isn't. The oxidation of that carbon pole will increase the current, and will alone furnish almost half enough electricity to decompose the alumina, leaving the other half, besides the part required to overcome the resistance, to be furnished by outside influence. The carbon poles will cost very little to replace; less than half a cent a pound for the alumina reduced.

"If ever an electrolytic process was invented that was feasible this is. The salt melts at a low red heat. I use the gasoline stove. It is very easily managed, does not fume or volatilize, or decompose from air or moisture (altogether unlike the double chloride). By it, the metal can be made purer than by any other process. Alumina, the oxide, is very easily made pure. The chloride always contains iron and silicon. Then, too, the oxide is the cheapest compound.

"Professor Jewett seemed to be quite excited, or a little bit excited, over what I showed him and told him last night. Perhaps he was wishing he had got out that himself.

"I have studied up the literature of the subject, and Jewett looked through one of his German books on electrolysis.

"I think this process is new. There is no mention of any such thing nor anything like it. Electrolyzing an infusible substance dissolved in a melted compound.

"You notice that the pamphlet of the Cowles Electric Smelting and Aluminum Co. says at the top of the third page that no chemist has yet succeeded in decomposing alumina by electricity. They did not get it into a liquid condition.

"What are we to do about this? More experiments ought

to be tried before going to the Patent Office. We ought to get someone who would assume risk and furnish money. I think you are inclined to offer too generous terms. What a patent is worth depends altogether on the way in which it is managed. If I were getting money on this, I would not offer anyone more than their money back with interest, and ask of the profits up to a certain limit, not any assignment of part of the invention.

"Then, too, in getting up a company, if it comes to that, we ought to have the help of lawyers who understand such matters. Patents go in for a larger share of the capital stock of a company than you think. I read of one formed by George Westinghouse where patents went in for $900,000 out of $1,000,000. We could probably find someone in Cleveland, if anywhere, on this thing. Doctor Brooks knows a great many men of money there. He is the family physician of the Cowles family and very intimate with them— has traveled with them. I mean Edwin Cowles and the rest of the *Leader* and the Aluminum Co. Probably you would rather attempt to do something in the East.

"Write me what you think. I must mail this letter.
Your aff. brother
Chas. M. Hall"

An exchange of letters followed in which Charles and George discussed the best means of raising money to cover the costs of securing patents and making a commercial test of the Hall process. Charles finally agreed to let George find a financial backer among his friends in Boston. While this tedious correspondence was inching its way through the mails, Charles kept busy in the woodshed laboratory.

He made a few preliminary trials which led him to believe

that a copper electrode was the answer to the anode problem. However, as the scale of his operations extended, he found this optimism was not justified and he returned to the use of the carbon anode, and the anodes are made of carbon even to this day.

Variations in the composition of the electrolyte offered a wider field for investigation and Charles tried the effect of adding other salts to the electrolyte. Cryolite is what is called a double fluoride of sodium and aluminum fluoride, and he found that he could make his electrolyte more fusible by adding either sodium or aluminum fluoride to the mixture. He seemed to prefer the addition of aluminum fluoride. He also tried the addition of either potassium or lithium fluoride and found certain advantages and disadvantages for each. Eventually, however, he came back to cryolite as the best basic composition with certain allowable variations in the ratio of the sodium to aluminum fluoride. All of this information was of course valuable in drawing broad patent claims as well as in operating his process to the best advantage.

By June, George had found a pair of somewhat timid backers and on the 30th Charles left for Boston. On arrival, Hall was introduced to Judge Henry Baldwin and a Mr. Brown. Hall's enthusiasm for the future of cheap aluminum which he was sure he could make by his new process won the interest of Baldwin and Brown. These two gentlemen decided to risk a couple of thousand dollars and advanced money to get Hall's first patent application under way. An arrangement, not very satisfactory to Hall, was soon effected. As Hall explained to his father:

"To get help, I had to give Baldwin and Brown one-third of the entire enterprise. They agreed to assist, etc., and to pay for patents to the extent of $1,500. They are likely to ask a larger share, as it will take more than $1,500 to get things started, but they won't get a larger share. I am chiefly concerned to make the thing work well and they will be willing to do anything to make their share valuable. Baldwin and Brown are really very fair sort of men."

Before starting work, Charles and his brother went to Washington, where they retained patent counsel to handle the patent situation. In a few days they returned to Boston and Hall started assembling the equipment necessary to demonstrate his invention on a larger scale than was possible in the family woodshed. He was able to secure a small dynamo of two or three horsepower, and set up small wrought iron reduction pots lined with carbon, about 4 inches in diameter and 12 inches deep. The judge's son, Dwight, volunteered his services as Charles's assistant; though inexperienced, he proved a willing worker. The equipment, however, was not received and ready for work until the latter part of August. By the second Sunday in September of '86, Charles was able to take time to tell his father the news:

"Dear Father:

"I received a letter and a card from you last week. I should probably have written to you before this, but Julia wrote to me just after I left home and has been writing ever since. As I am glad to get her letters I have to answer them and hard enough it is to answer them all. I think I am about four hundred behind now.

"I think my work has been getting on all right during the past week. There are some difficulties in working the process on a larger scale than I did at home. Some of them have been overcome and the rest will be. The Baldwins think so and I am sure of it.

"I have a room in Boston where I work. It is in the worst part of the town, perhaps not the worst, either. It is on the third floor of a block; the first floor is used for grocery stores, meat shops, etc., and the other two stories for manufacturing. Out of our window we see a four-story tenement house. It is very much the style, I imagine, of the New York tenement houses one reads of. A good many hardlooking people and queer sights are to be seen over there. Once Dwight Baldwin saw a boy beating his mother and an 'undressed kid' is quite a common sight. Our room is very near the Boston and Albany depot and is convenient on that account.

"I went into the city to church this morning to Trinity Church where Phillips Brooks preaches. The church is said to be one of the finest pieces of architecture in America, and I should not be surprised if it were. Inside it is magnificent; quite adapted to make the rustic stare, though I have seen a good many fine things and places since I left home. The service at Trinity is Episcopalian. Phillips Brooks is one of the famous preachers of the country. He had a very able discourse this morning. There are a number of fine churches in Boston that I am going to visit.

"I went to Cambridge this afternoon and have been there three times before. It is more like Oberlin there than in any other place near here. I rather like the looks of the people over there. The people that I meet in Allston are not representative Bostonians, that is to say, they are not literary. The judge is a graduate of Yale College and pretty well read, but the only papers and magazines he takes are the daily papers, the *Congregationalist,* and the *Andover*

Review. Mr. Brown, across the street, has been a business man all his life. He is very well informed as such men become and has a fine library.

"I am sorry you have not been well. I wish I could be of some assistance to you and the other members of the family. If this enterprise succeeds the family can keep a home in Oberlin. All the same, I think you better sell the N. Professor St. lot if you can get anything like the price paid for it. It will be better than borrowing money and paying both interest and taxes. If we should ever want to build a house on as expensive a lot as that we should have money enough to get that back or a better one. Tell Julia I will write her in a day or two.

Your aff. son

Chas. M. Hall"

In spite of Hall's optimism, the judge and his partner were disappointed because the amount of aluminum which Hall was making was so small. They couldn't seem to understand the difficulties inherent in working this process on a very small scale, and they were greatly concerned with the way the experiments were eating up their small available capital. This situation should not have been surprising, since a legal or even a business education did not provide much of a background for appraising a revolutionary metallurgical process. By October 23 the question of continuing the work had become critical, as Hall explained in his next letter to Julia:

"Dear Julia:

"Your letter with V. was received. George arrived here yesterday afternoon. He went to see Baldwin. The matter of my staying here another month is not yet settled, but I shall probably be home next week. Baldwin is not willing to furnish any more money at all. That is sure. George can't himself. Baldwin will talk with Brown tomorrow (Brown is now in Montreal). He says Brown may possibly be willing to set up the money but he don't think so and evidently won't advise him to. If Brown don't I will be home next week. Dwight Baldwin wants me to keep at work here another month and another six months. He talks of applying to his rich uncle or to someone else. If I get through with B & B I won't make another bargain here, won't stay here an hour longer than I can help.

"George said you and father advise him not to keep me here at work at his own expense. You gave him very good advice. Yesterday he asked me what I intended to do when my arrangement here was terminated. I told him I might take his invitation and go to Dover till I could find something else to do. He immediately said that it would cost me a good deal more to live there than in Oberlin and I had better go there. He has told me a number of times that if I failed here to come to Dover, but I have known that if he thought I failed he did not intend me to come there for a day, and I have not intended to go.

"I was not sick last Sunday but had the toothache and have had it worse and worse ever since till about two hours ago. One tooth that was filled very near the nerve bothered me a great deal and finally ulcerated and the side of my face swelled up as big as an apple. An ulcerated tooth is a terror, as perhaps you know. I had it pulled this morning when I concluded I had had enough of it. I should not have done so if you had not advised me to and the dentist had said that it was liable to be as bad again if it got well this time. Now my face is quite comfortable. Tomorrow I hope it will be reduced in size so as to be presentable.

The family have been quite commiserate. They know how it is themselves.

"George still insists that he has lost more than anyone else by this failure (to make anything under the contract with B & B). I think very likely it will turn but not as he thinks.

"He refused to give me credit for having risked anything or lost anything, says I have spent my time, but what else could I have done if I had not worked on this? Your brother evidently thinks that all the ability in the family is concentrated in himself. I wish matters had been settled up yesterday. It may be several days before they will be, I hope not long."

Charles's morale was being given a stern trial. Disappointment over the Baldwin-Brown failure was compounded by the defeatist attitude of brother George. This rift in relations between Charles and Julia, and brother George was one which was going to take years to heal. The ulcerated tooth added to the general gloom.

On October 27, Charles returned to Oberlin. In better spirits after a session at the piano, he counted the gains from the Boston episode: His patent application was safely filed and he had taken his first lesson in financing an invention. The scars were not serious, his faith in his process undiminished. Charles recalled with pleasure his many trips around historic Boston. He had visited with the Baldwin family and met interesting people at their home. Charles could see that his brother had given his best help, and there was nothing more to be hoped for in that quarter. Future events would prove the minister as poor a prophet as the judge.

Back in the woodshed, Hall started to work again to perfect

the operation of his process. Lacking money to purchase even a small dynamo, Hall improvised a much larger battery made from some twenty one-gallon and two-gallon earthenware jars and fitted with zincs which he cast himself. He investigated such details as additions to the basic cryolite electrolyte which might improve its efficiency.

Charles found Commencement at Oberlin College and his second class reunion in '87 a pleasant change from his experimenting. Much as he enjoyed these college visits, he was soon going to find himself so busy with his invention that he could attend reunions only infrequently.

While working in the woodshed laboratory, Hall took up again the search for a backer. This time he looked to Cleveland, where his uncle, Dr. Brooks, had a considerable acquaintance. With his uncle's help, arrangements were made for a conference between Hall and Messrs. Grasselli and Herrick, two men in the chemical business. The negotiations started with some promise, as Hall reported to Julia on July 7:

"I finally saw Mr. H. and Mr. G. together this morning. I think they will do something. They want to take in a third man and say if they can find one to suit and I will assign to the Co. ⅔ of all patents they will go on and put the thing in shape to form a company, etc., or they will take my original proposition, which was that I finally have ¼ the stock. They want a young man who will be able to give more time to the thing than they will, one who will be able to help me in the business of experiments, etc., and have in mind one whose father is rich and who is a chemist and has time to give to such a thing. Meantime if I will promise to agree to their terms they will lend me some money and have me see Gen. Leggett at once and be getting patent

71

matters in shape to apply for foreign patents, etc. I have not promised to agree as I want to see Dr. Brooks first. He is now at Rocky River at dinner with Mr. Eells. I have not heard from home yet. How are you all?"

But on the next day, Hall's report to Julia was keyed in a different tone:

"Every time I see H. and G. they appear more grasping and gobblesome. They now want a contract about like the Baldwin contract, substituting ⅔ for ½ and about $4,000 for $1,500. I don't know what I shall do with them, perhaps nothing finally. I have just been talking to Dr. Brooks about going to Maberry or the Cowles Co. if Grasselli and Herrick will not be more reasonable."

Dr. Brooks proved to be a practical adviser on business matters. This physician showed an understanding of men's minds as well as their bodies. Hall was also learning something about contracts:

"I had one (contract) all written out, at least in substance. . . . The contract is so made that if they back out at any time or refuse to carry out any of its provisions they are to have no share in the inventions and it so states. This Herrick kicks on. . . . I think it probable they will give what I ask if I manage them rightly and give them a little time to show that it don't make much difference. If not, they won't get anything. Dr. Brooks is becoming more and more disgusted with the way Grasselli has acted and still acts, his slowness and as now appears, his wanting to gobble me."

Although another man with money was brought into the picture, these negotiations came to nought. Hall's business education had progressed to the point where he refused to be "gobbled." Dr. Brooks now advised Hall to go to the Cowles Company with his invention.

The Cowles family, Edwin and his two sons, Eugene and Alfred, had gained some prominence by their invention and commercial exploitation of an electrothermal smelting process for making alloys containing aluminum in the range of 5 to 20 per cent. Aluminum bronze, an alloy containing about 90 per cent copper and 10 per cent aluminum was their most important product. This process was not an electrolytic process but a smelting process in which electric current was employed as the source of heat and carbon as the reducing agent. The aluminum alloys they could produce were limited, particularly with respect to their aluminum content; the process was not capable of producing pure aluminum. The Cowles people were in a good position to promote Hall's process for a variety of reasons. They were already in the aluminum alloy business, they had metallurgical experience, and they could readily provide experimental plant facilities for Hall in their works at Lockport, New York. This is Hall's own account of how he met Mr. Cowles:

"I went to see Mr. Alfred H. Cowles with the preliminary object of ascertaining whether the Cowles Company had a process for the manufacture of pure aluminum with which they were satisfied, and what the opportunity was of doing business with them. . . . I told him that I believed I had a process for producing pure aluminum at a cost of fifty cents per pound. . . . Mr. Cowles at the first interview did not seem particularly interested, and I left him with no intention of ever seeing him or his company on the subject again.

73

It was the next day, I believe, or very soon after, that Mr. Cowles called at the house of my uncle, Dr. M. L. Brooks, of Cleveland. He wished to learn whether I was still in the city and wanted, if possible, to see me again. He gave very flattering promises of what the Cowles Company would do for me if I had such a process as I claimed. The conversation was reported to me by my uncle, and it was under promises that any disclosures should be confidential, that shortly afterwards I saw Mr. Cowles at the office of the Cowles Company, and disclosed my invention to him. I showed him copies of these (patent) applications, specimens of pure aluminum and aluminum bronze that I had made at home and in Boston, told him about my interference suit with Heroult, all matters relating to the state of my applications in the Patent Office, what had been done with the invention practically, and gave all the information necessary for making business arrangements."

It did not take long to come to terms and on July 26, 1887, an agreement was effected by which Hall was to demonstrate his process at the Cowles' Lockport works. Hall was to receive $75 a month for his services and, after 90 days, the sum of $750 if they decided to continue the investigation. The Cowles Company received a six months' option to purchase the Hall patents for a one-eighth stock interest in the company as it would be reorganized if they decided to go on with the process. Hall packed up and went to Lockport.

One of Hall's laboratory notebooks for this period shows almost daily experiments beginning October 26, 1887, with the notation on the day before Christmas: "Dec. 24—No experiments on electrolysis." The work began again on January 2nd. On January 25th, Hall made the following report to the

Board of Directors of the Cowles Electric Smelting and Aluminum Company;

"I have now gained a thorough knowledge of the requirements of my process. It is now certain that very pure materials will not be required. The lack of success for a long time was due to improper mechanical arrangements and lack of adjustment of the current.

"I beg to state that the cost of apparatus and materials has been small, not over $150 to $200, that I have had the crudest apparatus and have worked entirely single-handed. In spite of this the process now appears to be under control, and I believe the knowledge has been gained by which to make it a success on any scale. It appears that in enlarging the operation no complicated problems will arise, but that by following a few simple principles success can be easily attained. Recently, over a pound of pure aluminum has been made. In order to make it pure and to make it more economically, all that is required is less crude apparatus. The prospect now is that the process is all that was supposed at the start. The results of the past six months' work will appear in the future development of the process."

The Cowles Company refused to pay Hall the $750 that was due him at the end of 90 days, and this was a great disappointment. However, for a consideration of $150, Hall extended the time for the payment of the $750 and the option period for another 90 days. At the end of this period the Cowles Company again failed to make payment and Hall extended the time for payment to April. Hall remained at Lockport, continuing his experiments at his own expense until July, 1888. The last notation in his notebook was made on July 10.

75

Hall family home on East College Street in Oberlin—
The Immortal Woodshed at the rear

The Cowles brothers' reputation as competent electrometallurgists seems inconsistent with their failure to hold this process, which was being laid on their metallurgical doorstep for such a modest consideration. A check of Hall's notebook shows that, even working on a very small scale, he had made as much as three-quarters of a pound of aluminum in a 7-hour period and with a current efficiency of 60 per cent. Even today, with all the improvements which have since been made in the process, the current efficiency runs only a bit above 80 per cent. It would be difficult to understand their judgment of Hall's process and their behavior toward Hall were it not for a letter written August 4, 1887, by Edwin Cowles, president of the company, to Mr. Baldwin of the same company, which reads in part:

"I think if you understood our reason for making the contract we did with Mr. Hall, you would not have objected to it. The young man submitted his process confidentially to Eugene and Fred, and they both said there was very great possibility of its having great merit, even to the extent of its being able to produce pure aluminum as low as 25 cents per pound. We reasoned as follows: If some parties were to get hold of his process, there might be great danger of its killing our process. As a matter of prudence, we concluded to make some experiments with it. We laid the matter before the Board and they were unanimously of the opinion that it was best that we should make the contract. To be sure, it will cost a few hundred dollars, but it is a good investment for us on the same principle that we would pay out the same amount to guard against losses by fire. The fact that the young man produced several buttons of aluminum on a kitchen stove alone is sufficient evidence that he might become a great inventor. The price we pay for it will be low if we can produce the pure metal at less than a dollar a pound, for we could, in that case, sell our foreign patents for half again as much, if not double or treble."

Hall's every effort with the Cowles brothers met with a discouraging response; the Cowles Company finally let their agreement lapse and with it their "fire insurance." Hall finally became convinced that this was a planned scheme to secure his patent at an even lower price. Letters and information which subsequently came to light strengthen this view. A Cowles letter (July 20, 1887) stated "we are now getting aluminum into alloys more cheaply than any other concern in the world," but they feared that anyone producing aluminum "for $8 per pound . . . could compete with us on our own alloys and make useless a part of our plant." Another Cowles letter stated that their process required 35 horsepower hours of electric energy to make a pound of aluminum in alloy form. Alfred Cowles's own calculations from Hall's experimental data showed that Hall was making pure aluminum for only 24.5 horsepower hours per pound. For many years after commercial operation was achieved, 15 horsepower per pound was not considered a bad figure. The promise of the Hall process was thus demonstrated even by the small-scale tests.

In this tense atmosphere, Hall stayed on at Lockport, experimenting at his own expense. When he finally decided to leave he was meticulously careful to make sure that the Cowles Company had no claim on him. He settled with Alfred Cowles for all the materials he had used in his own experiments since April 23.

From the work at Boston, at Lockport and in Oberlin, one conclusion was being inexorably forced upon Hall. Time was past for "pint scale" experiments. Hall knew he could make aluminum. What was needed was a pilot plant operation with competent engineering to explore the commercial possibilities of the process.

Friday the 27th of July, 1888 was Hall's last day in Lockport. Back at the boardinghouse, he dragged out his shabby black valise and carefully packed his notebooks and other records of his work. Then he tossed in his few belongings, snapped the bag shut, said good-bye to the landlady and was on his way to Oberlin.

Hall was not discouraged but left with high hopes. A friend he had made at Lockport was about to lead him to a man in

Pittsburgh who had vision, metallurgical experience, and business courage. "The young man (who) produced several buttons of aluminum on a kitchen stove" was to live long enough to make over 400,000,000 pounds of this precious metal.

6

. . . a patent, pretty as
a bank note

A GOOD PATENT is the constitutional diploma of the successful inventor. Ever since boyhood, Charles had yearned for that recognition and obtaining a patent on his invention was now urgent business on his calendar.

Early in July of '87 Charles and his brother George, left Boston on a trip to the United States Patent Office in Washington. Their first piece of business was to engage an attorney to handle the proposed patent application and Mr. Fenwick of Fenwick and Lawrence was Charles's choice. After asking innumerable questions regarding the details of Charles's discovery, Mr. Fenwick suggested that they visit the Patent Office and see what prior patents there might be in the general field of Hall's discovery. Charles's own account of this visit is rather prosaic and records none of the inner excitement which he experienced as he mounted the long flight of steps to the

Patent Office and walked through its dimly lighted halls to the office of one of the examiners:

> "At this time I spent several days in Washington and before filing an application for a patent, I had an interview with the Examiner who would have charge of this application, Dr. McLean; also with Dr. Antisell, Examiner in the Department of Chemistry. My brother and attorney were present at these interviews. We asked these Examiners to refer us to previous patents illustrating the state of the art; they consented to do so and for the purpose made a brief examination of American and foreign patents bearing on the electrolytic production of aluminum."

None of these patents anticipated the Hall invention in any way and it only took Mr. Fenwick a couple of days to complete an application and file it in the Patent Office on July 9, 1886.

Charles returned to Boston in a jubilant mood and started work on the installation of a small electrolytic cell to demonstrate the Hall process to his new-found backers. The failure of this promotional effort has already been told. He returned to Oberlin on October 27 and there soon reached him a communication from the Patent Office dated October 28.

Hall was stunned by the examiner's statement that "Claims 1 to 9 seem to be anticipated by the French Patent of April 23, 1886, Héroult, for electrolyzing a solution of alumina in molten cryolite." This was the first time Hall had ever seen the name Héroult and he awaited anxiously the receipt of a copy of the Héroult French patent which his attorney secured as soon as possible. The patent confirmed his worst fears; Héroult was claiming substantially the same invention that he had made. Not even Fenwick's optimistic opinion that he would prevail over Héroult could completely dispel the apprehension which gripped his mind. However, he had new plans for work in his woodshed laboratory and the combination of physical and mental activity became so absorbing that he had little time left for worrying about Héroult.

In January Hall made another trip to Washington to consult with his attorneys on strategy. On his arrival he sent Julia a brief note with the information that he had taken a sleeping car from Pittsburgh to Washington but had not slept much during the night. Whether the patent problems occupying his mind had crowded out sleep or whether the jolting of the car was responsible is not known. The news, however, that he had found a room in which to stay for fifty cents a day is just another reminder of the financial problems with which Charles had to struggle.

To meet the situation created by the Héroult French patent, Hall filed an affidavit stating that he had completed his invention prior to April 23, 1886; he also submitted with the affidavit a specimen of the aluminum obtained by his process. For the moment this satisfied the Patent Office and they proceeded with their regular examination of Hall's application. Apparently the Patent Office was not very busy at the time, for in a period of less than twelve months, Hall received through his attorneys, twelve communications from the patent examiner.

On June 8, 1887, Hall was notified that an Interference was about to be declared between his application and the application which Paul L. T. Héroult had filed in the United States on May 22, 1886. Hall then made another trip to Washington to confer with his attorneys.

This Interference action was to prove another step in the education of our woodshed inventor. The precautions which

Hall had taken to establish the exact dates on which he had completed the various steps of his invention were most fortunate. Through the testimony of his sister Julia who had witnessed his experiments, and through the letters which he wrote his brother George, Charles established clearly the important dates of February 16 and February 23 as the ones on which he reduced his invention to practice. This evidence was supplemented by the testimony of Professor Jewett to whom he had shown the nuggets of aluminum which he produced on that historic date. Héroult was a foreign inventor and by Patent Office rules was limited in his proof to the filing date of his French patent of April 23, 1886. Motion and countermotions kept the Interference before the Patent Office for a year, but on July 10, 1888, the issue was decided in Hall's favor. His attorneys then proceeded to put the application in condition for allowance. In the meantime Hall had filed several other applications covering various details of his process with the objective of securing the broadest possible protection for his invention.

Five patents were issued to Hall on April 2, 1889. One can readily understand the joy of an aspiring inventor when he receives the accolade of the Patent Office through the granting of his first patent. Hall gave expression to this pleasure when he wrote Julia the good news:

> "Our patents were issued Tuesday. I saw them one day last week all done up in gold lettering, blue ribbon, etc., was as pretty as a new bank note."

Julia's response was enthusiastic and had an unexpected effect upon her brother:

> "I wish you would not send me any more compliments.

Charles Martin Hall at age of twenty-seven

After I read the last ones I started to shave and I guess my head was turned. Anyway, I was not paying attention to what I was doing and cut a piece out of my nose."

The patent was a grant by the United States government of a legal monopoly for a period of seventeen years for the production of aluminum by the Hall process. Hall was to learn, however, that this was a grant which might have to be defended at great expense. The technical problems of building a new industry were to be complicated by the legal worries of patent litigation. This, however, is getting somewhat ahead of the story.

In 1911, Hall and Héroult met face to face in a dramatic setting. It was a happy occasion for Hall because he was being presented with one of chemistry's highest honors—the Perkin Medal. Héroult attended the dinner and ceremony which were held in New York. After Hall had spoken, Héroult was introduced and reminisced on the growth of the aluminum industry. He closed his remarks with these gracious words:

"My friend Hall and myself have been fighting for fifteen years, most of the shots going wild on account of the long range over the Atlantic Ocean. Since we met, however, we conceived a better opinion of each other, and I take great pleasure tonight in extending to my friend Hall my sincere congratulations on the award to him of the Perkin Medal."

7

. . . ladles out the first aluminum

IN THE YEAR 1872, Leander Hunt and his wife Mary, of Hyde Park, Massachusetts, a suburb of Boston, were debating an important question in family council: Should their son Alfred be sent to college or should he secure his training in the School of Experience? Of course Alfred wanted to be a metallurgist for he had grown up next door to the Douglas Axe Works in East Douglas, Massachusetts. Hunt's Superior Axes, a product of the Works founded by his grandfather, Oliver Hunt, had long been famous among New England's woodchopping pioneers.

James Park, Jr., a friend who was visiting the Hunts, strongly recommended practical experience instead of college theories to start the boy on his career. "Send him to me in Pittsburgh," said Mr. Park, "and I will teach him more in three months about making steel than he can learn in four years of college."

His mother was not convinced that such a short cut to metallurgy would be a sound basis for the broad technical career she sought for her son. She wanted nothing but the best scientific training available for Alfred. She had studied chemistry at Patapsco Institute, and taught the subject there after graduation. Mary Hanchet Hunt was a very literate Temperance Advocate, and was one of the emancipated women of her day. She was also a determined woman. So Alfred studied metallurgy and chemistry at Massachusetts Institute of Technology.

After graduation in 1876, young Hunt spent five years putting into practice the training he had acquired in college. First he worked for a year at the Bay State Iron Works making steel in the open-hearth furnace. With this practical experience as a background, Alfred went to the Nashua Iron & Steel Company where he was put in charge of chemical and metallurgical work for the open-hearth department. For a period of three years he was learning to manage both steel and men, and his latent executive talent had a fine opportunity for development.

Living in Nashua, New Hampshire, was a memorable and happy period, for while there he married comely, dark-eyed Maria McQuesten in 1878. However, Hunt saw greater opportunity in the west and in 1881, he went to Pittsburgh, the rising steel center of the nation. The James Park who had advised against college, was now glad to have this young man's technical training in metallurgy and chemistry at his service and made him superintendent of the open-hearth department at the Black Diamond Steel Works of Park, Brother & Co.

Alfred Ephraim Hunt began to make a name for himself as a metallurgist and decided to try his wings in independent

91

practice. In 1882 he formed a partnership with another young chemist named George H. Clapp, for the inspection of steel structures and the testing of materials. They associated themselves with the Pittsburgh Testing Laboratory and became proprietors of its chemical department in 1883. In the year 1887, Hunt and Clapp acquired sole ownership of the Pittsburgh Testing Laboratory. The integrity and high caliber of their technical services helped the Laboratory flourish and it stands today, a leader in the field.

Alfred Hunt was quite properly addressed as "Captain." Even as a student he had enlisted in the Ninth Massachusetts Infantry and soon earned a captaincy. His interest in military science and tactics began with a course in the subject at Massachusetts Institute of Technology, and he commanded a company of the Institute Battalion. After moving to Nashua, Hunt enlisted in the New Hampshire Militia and in a period of seven months, rose from sergeant to captain. In Pittsburgh his energies were absorbed at first in getting a start as a metallurgist, but his enthusiasm as an organizer was irrepressible. He was soon engaged in starting Battery B, and enlisted as a private in its ranks. In a few months he was elected captain, and he carried the title with distinction throughout life, in both peace and war. He was a natural leader in every activity he undertook.

In personal appearance, Alfred Hunt was of medium height, with brown hair, hazel eyes, dark complexion and a striking black mustache. A friend, Albert R. Ellis who became president of the Pittsburgh Testing Laboratory in 1936, lived next door to the Hunt family when he was a small boy. Ellis carries a vivid recollection of Captain Hunt as "a quick, energetic and driving personality, but withal a genial, kindly man, fond of small boys. And, as he occasionally appeared dressed in his uniform and wearing a sword, the eyes of childhood sometimes grew big with wonder and with pride that one knew him."

Hunt had some knowledge of aluminum and a considerable interest in the new metal. He had an idea that with the very high temperatures reached in the open-hearth furnace, he might be able to reduce alumina with carbon and secure metallic aluminum; so he hired a young man named Romaine Cole to conduct the experiments he planned. Cole told of his work in these words:

"These experiments consisted mainly in determining what effect the exceedingly high temperature, which is possible to attain in the open-hearth furnace, had on aluminum oxide in the presence of carbon, and also in the presence of carbon together with other metals, to serve as a bath, and to catch the aluminum as it was reduced from the ore. The hearth and roof of my furnace were constructed of magnesia brick, a material far more refractory than silica brick, as the temperature to which I attained would have melted down the interior of said furnace had it been constructed of a less refractory material than magnesia. I venture to say that we obtained, in this work, probably the highest temperatures ever before secured in any open-hearth process; but, after spending considerable money, we found that the effect of carbon on alumina under the highest temperatures attainable in this style furnace, and under the most favorable conditions possible, was practically nil."

Later, Romaine Cole had a job with the Cowles Electric Smelting and Aluminum Company while Hall was demonstrating his electrolytic process at their Lockport Works. Cole's duties were to visit the Cowles customers and instruct them in the application and handling of their aluminum bronzes and other alloys containing about 10 per cent of aluminum.

He became acquainted with Hall in the summer of 1888 and had the opportunity of observing his process in operation on a small scale. Through watching the work and discussion, Cole soon acquired some of Hall's enthusiasm for its possibilities. When at last Hall decided to waste no more time on the Cowles Company, he sent Cole to Pittsburgh to lay the process before Captain Hunt.

Back in Pittsburgh, Cole had no difficulty in securing Hunt's attention. He was well informed about the market for the Cowles alloys, and many talks with Hall had convinced him of the advantages of producing pure aluminum instead of alloys with only the minor content of aluminum to which Cowles was limited. From watching Hall produce aluminum by his new process, he knew that it was practical. With this background, Cole proved himself a good negotiator. Hall kept in touch with his agent by letter. Particularly anxious to profit by past experience, he wrote Cole to insist on starting "to work in a moderately large business way, without waiting for any more of these little experiments." Cole's suggestion of $15,000 capital seemed to Hall to be a good amount to begin with.

With the facts before him, it did not take Captain Hunt long for appraisal and decision. On July 31, he called an organization meeting at his home on Shady Lane, East Liberty. Attending this meeting were six other young Pittsburgh industrialists. Captain Hunt's enthusiasm for the new venture was persuasive. The group decided to form the Pittsburgh Aluminium Company—a name soon changed to The Pittsburgh Reduction Company. Soon after formation, the Company adopted the spelling *aluminum*. Several committees were appointed and ordered to report at the next meeting.

As soon as Charles learned that Hunt was prepared to

promote the Hall process if the representations made by Cole were confirmed, he left Oberlin for Pittsburgh to complete the negotiations. Cole had already engaged a room for Charles at his own boardinghouse in East Liberty, a suburb of Pittsburgh. After Charles had unpacked his valise, brushed off travel dust and made his person as presentable as possible, the pair left for a conference with Captain Hunt. Cole brought Hall up to date on the Pittsburgh situation during their walk to the Hunt residence.

When Hall was introduced, Captain Hunt could scarcely believe his eyes. How could this mere boy have made the revolutionary discovery whose commercial potential had gripped his imagination? For his part, Hall received from the firm grip of the captain's welcoming hand and the steady appraising gaze of his kindly hazel-brown eyes, an impression of a man sure of himself, and a man from whom he could expect both understanding and fair treatment. Captain Hunt's appearance and manner of speaking befitted a man both accustomed to lead and to command. He wasted no time on small talk but asked Hall to tell him about his process.

"Cole told me," said Hall, "about your failure to reduce alumina with carbon, and I had the same experience in similar experiments. I thought of electrolyzing molten alumina but I had no way of melting this almost infusible oxide. Success came, however, when I discovered that I could lower the melting point of alumina sufficiently by dissolving it in molten cryolite. Then I found, as I had hoped, that I could pass an electric current through this solution and separate metallic aluminum from the oxygen in the alumina."

"What happens to the cryolite?"

"It is not decomposed by the electric current," continued Hall, "and I only have to add more alumina from time to

95

time as the alumina is used up. My experiments show without a doubt, that I can make pure aluminum at a much lower cost than by any other known process. I am sure now that I can produce aluminum for less than a dollar a pound and after a little experience with commercial operation of my process I will be able to reduce the cost to fifty cents or less. You know of course that aluminum is selling now for eight dollars a pound. What we must do first is build a plant which is large enough to give us operating experience on a commercial scale."

"That is the conclusion I have reached," was Hunt's reply, "and I have made arrangements with a small group of friends to join me in this venture. But first of all we must be sure that you are going to secure a patent which will protect us while we are building up the business."

Captain Hunt had breathed deeply of the atmosphere of industrial adventure which was responsible for the amazing growth of Pittsburgh as a manufacturing center, but he had not lost the prudent foresight characteristic of his New England forebears. Although Hall assured him that his patents were in good hands and that he had just received a decision from the Patent Office which removed Héroult as a threat to the Hall applications, Captain Hunt insisted on taking his own attorney, Mr. Walcott, and Hall to Washington for a personal investigation of the patent situation.

George Clapp, Hunt's partner in the Pittsburgh Testing Laboratory, was on his way home from Europe when the decision was reached to form a company and promote the Hall process. When the two met after Mr. Clapp landed, Captain Hunt greeted him with the news:

"This will surprise you, George, but you are now in the aluminum business. I have formed a company to promote a new process invented by a young man from Ohio, and I have put you down for a share in the enterprise."

Joining Hunt and Clapp in the plans to promote Hall's process were four young friends, three of them engaged in the steel business: Howard Lash, head of Carbon Steel Company; Millard Hunsiker, general sales manager of Carbon Steel Company; and Robert Scott, superintendent of one of the Carnegie Steel Company's mills; also W. S. Sample, who was already associated with Hunt and Clapp as chief chemist of the Pittsburgh Testing Laboratory. The other two men who attended the first meeting decided the venture was too risky for their money.

Both Hall and Cole attended the next meeting of the group, which was held on the afternoon of August 8 in the 33rd Street offices of Carnegie Phipps and Co. During the week since the first meeting, the appointed committees had been quite busy. Chairman Hunt reported for the Committee on Patents:

> "that Mr. Walcott, Mr. Hall and Mr. Hunt had been in Washington and found the patents in good shape for being taken out in the United States and that they should be taken out in England, France, Germany, Italy, Spain, Belgium, Norway and Sweden, Denmark, Russia and Austria."

Mr. Sample reported for the Committee on Organization:

> "that the committee recommended organizing a company under the Laws of the State of Pennsylvania and for a capital of twenty thousand ($20,000) dollars."

Mr. Lash reported for the Committee on Plant:

> "that after looking over several locations the most de-

sirable seemed to be the ground on Smallman Street between Thirty-third and Thirty-second Streets. A twenty-five by one hundred and twenty-five foot lot could be leased for about two hundred and fifty (250) dollars a year with taxes. A building 25' x 16' x 60' could be put up for about four or five hundred dollars."

"Mr. Clapp reported that a 125 HP Westinghouse engine with two steel return flue boilers with feed water heater and all attachments complete and set up on foundations built by the company would cost about six thousand (6,000) dollars."

According to the minutes, the reports were accepted and the committees continued with instructions to report best action to take in regard to plant, at the next meeting to be held at 9:30 a.m. on August 10.

Events moved fast in Pittsburgh. On August 10, the Committee on Organization reported,

"that all the stock had been subscribed for by Scott, Lash, Hunsicker, Clapp and Sample, and that progress was making in securing charter and agreement with Hall and Cole."

On August 14 the company accepted bids for two Westinghouse dynamos, rated at 1,200 amperes each at 25 volts, for $2,800 installed. On August 21, the directors authorized the lease of a lot on Smallman Street. The Committee on Plant was authorized to contract for the erection of an iron-clad building 24' x 16' x 70' and for a steam plant comprising two steel boilers and a Westinghouse engine.

The planning and construction work absorbed all of Hall's time; he worked night and day at the many jobs before him. Placing an order for the two large Westinghouse dynamos gave him particular pleasure. A large current of electricity is required to produce a pound of aluminum; even in present practice it takes a current of about 1,600 amperes for an hour to make a pound of aluminum. The batteries Hall used at Oberlin supplied enough current to make small beads or buttons of aluminum. At Lockport, he had a dynamo supplying 250 amperes and made 6 to 12 ounces of aluminum in a short day's run. Now, with a current of more than 2,000 amperes in prospect, Hall could look forward to continuous production of pound after pound. Is it any wonder that the aluminum industry, with its Gargantuan appetite for electric power, had to wait for the dynamo before it could flourish?

With all his activities from one end of the week to the other, Hall missed writing to Julia on many a Sunday. However, on September 16 he took time for a hurried note telling of progress being made at the Smallman Street works, and "small talk" about living in Pittsburgh:

"Dear Julia,

"I dare say if I didn't write home today you would think I was dead and be having my will probated; so to save you any embarrassment from a mistake like that I must write something. Our building is nearly finished but the machinery is not in. Captain Hunt says he allows us till the 15th of October to get to making aluminum, so you must not expect much very definite before that.

"I spoke to Cole about changing our boarding place and finding rooms and board near our works; the subject has been considered several times. We have looked up one lady who was highly recommended to us. She would give us room and board for five dollars a week apiece and was sure we would like it. She and Mr. Boyle had been in the saloon

99

and boardinghouse business for 20 years. She told a pitiful story about the difficulties of the 'license business.' It has become very risky and they had been obliged to give it up. I had to laugh to hear her talk, specially about the saloon business. Since then, Cole said he was in favor of staying at East Liberty, he didn't 'want to live in Hell.' Now, however, he is more in favor of changing than I am, principally on account of expense. He has to send $40 or $50 a month to his grandparents, and he has a more expensive room than I have. Yesterday I went to look in a rather better place than where Mrs. Boyle lives. We can get good rooms and board in a respectable neighborhood, about a mile from our works, for $5.00 a week, but I don't like it and believe it will be better for me to stay here. This month won't cost me more than $40, including everything, out of my $90. This is a nice neighborhood and the other is not. I haven't got a piano yet but am going to get one this week if possible.

"Cole has gone to Cleveland to do some testifying for the Cowles Company in a lawsuit. They pay his expenses. I am coming to the conclusion that he is the same kind of fellow I first thought him. I don't know of his drinking anything alcoholic but twice in a month and a half. In that respect he is no different from others.

"I have made the acquaintance of the minister's daughter across the street and am invited to call.

"I think I have written enough to prove that I am still living.

Your aff. brother,

C. M. Hall"

Having charted the company's course, Captain Hunt was impatient to get started, but the plant was not ready for operation on October 15. On the Sunday before Thanksgiving, Hall was sure it would be only a few days more before they could start making aluminum. It was in a mood appropriate to the season that he went to church and later wrote Julia:

Pittsburgh, Pa., Nov. 25, 1888

"Dear Julia,

"I have been to church just now and so have not much time to write you. I am quite sleepy. Next week I won't go to church and will write you a long letter. . . . Our plant is now almost ready to start. They were going to start it yesterday but a steam pipe cracked and had to be fixed. That has already been repaired. Everything is about ready and Tuesday we may be making Al almost certainly Wednesday. I shall stay here for Thanksgiving and probably work. Once last week I stayed at the shop till twelve o'clock at night and last night till about ten, that was for baking the carbon linings in our pots.

"I was asked Friday to give my price for some of my stock. Some of Hunt's friends want to buy. If next week's work goes well that stock will sell for par ready money and inside of six months it will be worth 200%, so I didn't give any price. . . . Both our dynamos are in and they look very nice. The copper conductors to the furnaces are 4 inches by half an inch and weigh altogether over a thousand pounds. We had more good reports from patents last week. The lawyer appealed against an unfavorable decision of the examiner and knocked him out. Louie's letter was very nice. I will try and write a better one myself before long.

Your aff. brother

C. M. Hall"

The day before Thanksgiving, the gas fires were lighted

Alfred Ephraim Hunt—photograph taken in Nashua, New Hampshire, about the year 1880

under the reduction pots and everything made ready to start making aluminum. When the cryolite bath in the pot was molten, the engine and dynamos were started, and the current started flowing to the carbon anodes suspended in the bath.

To help operate the new works, Capt. Hunt had given Hall a young assistant. He also was a minister's son and had just graduated from Amherst. His father, the Rev. Perley Davis, had known Captain Hunt in Boston, but the coming of Arthur

102

Vining Davis to Pittsburgh is best told as Mr. Davis himself has related the story:

"It was the first day of September, 1888, that I—just graduated from college—arrived in Pittsburgh to work for Captain Hunt, whose family and mine had been friends in the East for many years. On account of this friendly relation with my new employer, Captain Hunt had undertaken to secure me a room and so on my arrival in Pittsburgh he took me to the house in which this room had been secured and in which he had previously secured a room for Mr. Hall, who had himself only a few weeks before arrived in Pittsburgh. Although at that time it was not intended or expected that I should engage in the aluminum business or be in any way connected with Mr. Hall's work, yet in order that I might have a friend living under the same roof, after Captain Hunt had shown me to my room he took me across the hall to the room occupied by Mr. Hall and after Captain Hunt had introduced us he left us, and I remember that Mr. Hall and I spent the evening together, as indeed we did most of the evenings for the next three months. Three months later the experimental plant to exploit Mr. Hall's process was ready for operation, at which time I became connected with the work and thereafter for the next year Mr. Hall and I alternated in charge of the day and night work but always overlapping our stay at the plant both in the morning and in the evening for an hour or two. It thus happened that from the very beginning of Mr. Hall's work and from the beginning of our business careers it has been my good fortune to be closely associated with Mr. Hall."

Through the night and Thanksgiving Day, Hall and Davis anxiously watched the pots and speculated on the outcome of the first day's run. Hall knew from previous experience that the pots were making aluminum, for he could see the gas

103

bubbling around the anodes as the oxygen, electrolytically separated from the alumina, reacted with the carbon to form carbon dioxide. The aluminum, heavier than the molten bath, should be collecting on the carbon lining at the bottom of the pot. Finally their curiosity could be restrained no longer. Hall ladled out the company's first aluminum and cast a small ingot of the silvery metal in a small sand mold.

When the aluminum was cool enough to handle, Hall and Davis took turns, hefting it, admiring it, and examining it from every angle. When they had wrung the last thrill from their precious chunk of aluminum, it was twilight. Both were tired and hungry. Davis opened the office safe, carefully placed the little ingot inside, closed and locked the ponderous door. "Let's go eat," he said!

8

*. . . aluminum is piling
up in the office*

IF THIS WERE an Horatio Alger story, Hall should now marry the girl of his dreams and go on to fame and fortune. But the road to wealth and honors was beset by many dragons —technical, commercial and legal—which had to be overcome before the goal was reached.

The reduction pot which produced aluminum on Thanksgiving Day operated for a week, then sprang a leak and was shut down for repairs. This accident Hall attributed to the action of the gas flame heating the iron shell. When working with his process on a small scale, Hall kept the cryolite bath molten by heating the outside of the reduction pot. He believed, however, that as soon as he could operate on a commercial scale, the "waste heat" of the electrolyzing current would enable him to dispense with external heating. This he had told Julia as early as August of 1886. The time for trial of this practice was close at hand.

December 9th, 1888

"Dear Julia:

"All the first part of the day after breakfast I spent at Captain Hunt's. He asked me to go to church with them and afterwards to stay to dinner. A very nice man is the captain. Now it is nearly five and after supper I have to go to our works and get things started for morning. Our experiment lasted till Wednesday morning, when it appeared best to quit in order to make changes and because the pot was leaking. Everybody is convinced of the success of the scheme, and although we are not making 60 lbs. a day right along, as calculated, no one expected it, and all express themselves as pleased. I got credit for more than was really due, because Monday and Tuesday nights I really got pretty good sleep on the office desk while I made my man Friday attend to things with orders to call me if anything went wrong. I think there is no doubt now of our success. . . . Cole is probably going to sell out to Hunt and his friends.

Your aff. brother

C. M. Hall"

Charles was too busy on the next Sunday to write his sister or even to attend church. It was Tuesday evening before he told Julia the latest news:

"I have not had the most brilliant luck at the works the past week. . . . Leaky pots are not going to be a drawback much longer as we are going to dispense with heat on the outside, use thick linings to retain the heat of the current and depend on that. This has been tried twice already and the current gave heat enough when confined and some very pure aluminum was made but the pot wasn't shaped just

107

right for good circulation and even heating so we had to quit, and will try again.

"I sleep nights now instead of working. Captain Hunt got Davis to take my place when we work nights. He is the boy from Boston and fresh from Amherst College who had the room next to mine for a while. He has a good deal of ability as well as grit to stand it working all night in the dirt and soot and worse, the fumes that he has to endure sometimes. The last night he was there he said he had a h-l of a night, and I am sure he did. He takes it all good-naturedly, however. I am not coming home Christmas."

It took time and experimentation to get the new-style pots operating satisfactorily. Some of the stockholders complained of the delay, but Charles never let disappointing results shake his faith in the ultimate success of the process. By the middle of January, 1889, he was able to tell Julia:

"I have to work all tonight (Saturday) and hope to sleep tomorrow so will write home now. I have only a minute. I have worked nights this week and Davis has worked day-times. We have both spent 14 or 15 hours a day. . . . I have had very good luck the past week. Our first pot made 10 pounds of metal in two days, next about 20 in four days, next nothing, next nothing or very little, next less than three pounds in four days, next 120 pounds in six days; that was completed yesterday. (We only calculated 15 per day with full current, which we have not used.) Now we have two going. When these pots were doing so badly the Co. lost faith and sent for me. I had the mixture all right if the pot had been heated from the bottom, but when heated by the current a mixture that would dissolve much more alumina was needed. This has just recently been found out and now I have a combination that will probably do easily twice what we anticipated. The whole thing is working out far better and simpler than I ever hoped and I believe now that we have a magnificent invention. Inside of a month I expect to see these works making $100 a day above expenses—Davis says $400. You know there is only about $12,000 invested. It is only Wednesday of this week that Hunt told me that two of the Co. were wanting to sell and others were shaky. If they want to sell I advise someone to buy them out. I think they will change their minds, however. The way our last pot chewed up the alumina and reduced it was almost enough to frighten one—some days 50 pounds. One going now starts out better. The difference is in the mixture for dissolving alumina."

Romaine Cole had done important service in bringing Hall and Hunt together. For this help, Hall agreed to give Cole a share of any return the patents might bring. This was a bargain which Hall kept. Cole, however, was not made of the same stuff as Hall and Davis. Although given ample opportunity, Cole failed to make a place for himself in the young organization and on December 12, owing to illness, his services in helping manage operations were terminated. Later, his experience as a traveling service man for the Cowles Company suggested that Cole would be helpful in getting some badly needed business for The Pittsburgh Reduction Company. While on such a mission in the East, Hall kept in touch with Cole by correspondence. These letters, running through 1889, contain some interesting news about the progress of The Pittsburgh Reduction Company.

Gradually, the technical problems plaguing the reduction pots were brought under control. However, the solution of these problems brought on a crisis of another kind—the problem of overproduction. In June, Hall wrote Cole:

> "I hope you will succeed in getting a good outlet for our metal. It is piling up in the office at the rate of thirty to fifty pounds a day. I saw the aluminum match cases you sent. They look very good indeed."

This accumulation of aluminum was the cause of serious concern to the management. Although Hall's job as superintendent was to produce as much aluminum as possible, his interests as a stockholder were much broader. His views on the situation, as disclosed in another letter to Cole in August, show how his business education was progressing. They are also significant as an early expression of farseeing policies which were to subordinate immediate profit for future growth of the company and the aluminum industry:

> "The plant is doing very well now. This month, of which two days remain, will see a production of 1,300 lbs. aluminum, all but 40 lbs. No. 1 metal. . . . I wish the sales department was in as good a condition. Mr. Clapp told me this morning that we had sold up to date about $3,000 of metal, a pretty poor showing.
>
> "We have got to do a great deal more than we have done to make it profitable and easy for people to use our metal. That is, put the price down and sell sheets, rods, etc., at just what it costs above the ingot metal. We want this metal out of the office—over two tons right here now—making aluminum popular.
>
> "I am not in favor of putting the price below what we finally intend to put the output of a big plant. But I am in favor of getting a big business in making and selling alumi-

num by every means which will hasten it, and am entirely in favor of throwing up the chance of making a big per cent on a small amount if it will hasten the time when we can sell a large amount at a moderate profit. . . . Will it increase our sales to any considerable extent to put the price down to $2.00 or $2.50? Will it help the introduction of the metal in the many new uses to which it must be put if we are ever to make any money?"

And in September:

"In regard to the price of our metal. It is agreed among the Co. that to get an increased demand and market is far more important than profits on sales, and that we must do something to get rid of our present stock faster."

By November, Hall was talking about selling aluminum for $1.50 or even $1.00 a pound. Production at the Smallman Street plant continued to boom, and the company's directors had lively discussions regarding the best selling price for aluminum. The company's initial successes with their process were attracting attention and there were ominous rumors of legal action by the Cowles Company, which apparently was beginning to feel the competition from the Hall aluminum. News along these lines featured Hall's letter of September 14 to Cole:

"I came home Friday for a day or two and will be back in Pittsburgh Wednesday. I saw Tucker and learned all he had to tell about our being sued. It is Eugene's (Cowles) idea. . . . At present, so far as their own patents are concerned, I understand they claim a monopoly of the electric current for heating for metallurgical purposes.

"The plant last week made 385 pounds of metal, this

111

Smallman Street Works of The Pittsburgh Reduction Company

week I think it will run a little above that. The cost of production is now down to about 65 cents per pound in this little plant. Even with steam power we could get the cost here in Pittsburgh down to 40 cents per pound, this is less than half the Cowles cost of production at present, but you know about this as well as I."

When The Pittsburgh Reduction Company was first organized, the plan was to raise $20,000 capital to build and operate a small plant to determine the value of the Hall patents. The initial subscription of $20,000 capital was paid by the stockholders, on the installment plan, five or ten per cent at a time. Sixty per cent of the total had been paid in by April 5, and it was made 100 per cent on the first day of July. In fact, the company's expenses were running so high that another $10,000 had to be subscribed. The original plan was to recapitalize the company when the operations at Smallman Street proved the process practical and warranted expansion of the business. This seemed to be the time.

In September the stockholders authorized an increase of the capital stock of the company to one million dollars. This change was effected on October 2, 1889. The initial division of the 10,000 shares of stock was as follows: Hall, 3,525 shares and Cole, 1,000; Hunt, Clapp, Hunsiker, Lash, Sample and Scott, 3,006 shares. Four other men subscribed for 169 shares, and 2,300 shares remained in the company's treasury for future sale. During the next two years, Hall, Hunt and Clapp maintained their stockholdings with little change except for family transfers. The treasury stock was sold, and thirty-five new names added to the list of stockholders. Cole gradually disposed of his stock, the last share in January, 1893; Hall bought 35 shares from Cole, and the rest went to nine new stockholders.

The expansion mood had taken hold of Hall when he wrote to Cole on November 29:

"As to enlarging the plant, I have thought about that a good deal and it seems to me time to think about it at least. To secure an output of 2,000 pounds a week will require from $25,000 to $30,000 at the outside. . . . With this enlarged plant we can make Al for 40 cents per pound, including office expenses, taxes, insurance, etc., and everything. Hunt says 37 cents against 43 cents now. I think we can see sale for 3,000 pounds now if the price were $1.00 or $1.50 per pound and with that price the demand should advance rapidly. . . . For my part I believe too that the only way to build up an immense and secure business is to lower our prices to something like that I mentioned and perhaps even lower. I think we are going in time to make Al for 20 cents per pound or less. The large expenses are ore, power, and interest on the plant. The ore is surely coming way down. We can get it now for three cents per pound. Electric power too is coming down some. 'Everyone' says in time we will get electricity directly from the oxidation of coal. I have special reasons for thinking it will be inside a year or two."

The last three sentences are a sly reference to the battery project which Hall had become interested in seven years before and which still claimed his attention whenever he had a little spare time.

If Hall was not yet a rich inventor, he was on the way to becoming one. He certainly was an inventor, and he valued his stockholding in The Pittsburgh Reduction Company at over three hundred thousand dollars. Now he was not just satisfied with having someone else promote his process. Although a director and vice-president of his company, he worked long hours at the plant, determined that the success of his process and The Pittsburgh Reduction Company should far exceed any of his original prophecies.

The Smallman Street works was located in a district now known as The Strip, a strip of land a couple of blocks wide, lying between the Allegheny River and a bleak hill, with a barrenness common to industrial Pittsburgh. The clamor of steel mills, the grim streets and the grimy people living in the neighborhood tested the endurance of the boy who loved the green fields and tree-shaded avenues of Oberlin. Contacts with neighbors were sometimes anything but casual:

"I had a real bit of diversion last week. I pummeled a

boy near our works and raised a big rumpus. He is the worst kid around there, about fifteen years old and often throws stones at us and the building. Last week he was throwing sand at the building and into the steam pipes and would not stop when I told him, so I pulled him down and gave him a mild thrashing. It raised the whole neighborhood. His father, who keeps a saloon without a license, came over and was going to sue me, and his mother came and put in her tongue. I think it did them good, however, for we have not been bothered with the kids nearly so much since."

Not only were the boys outside the plant annoying, but some of the men working inside were problem children. Hobbs was a young man hired to work in the pot room. According to Hall:

"Hobbs is here and is not much good and a more disgusted and disillusioned boy I don't think you could find. He told one of the other workmen that he never expected to have to work so hard. Davis is a good boy and is doing very well."

A week later Charles wrote Julia about a different kind of management problem:

"I am sorry to tell you that I had to discharge Henry L—— or 'fire' him as they say, a month ago and more. He didn't keep on doing as well as at first and he used to walk through our belts in the engine room. Those belts travel over three miles a minute and if Henry had been caught in one of them I think we would have had to scrape him up with a knife."

In contrast to the occasional excitement attending the extinguishing of a fire in the pot room, there were episodes with a humorous angle which helped relieve the tensions caused by unexpected pot behavior. A half century later, Davis still recalled some of these happenings.

"I remember one day when Bucher was doing something around the two furnaces or pots as we called them, and I asked him what he was doing and he said, 'I am taking a volt out of this pot and putting it into the other one.' Our prize package, however, was the one and only laborer that we had whose name was Mike. My most vivid recollection of Mike is in connection with the manufacture of aluminum fluoride which we used to make by mixing alumina and hydrofluoric acid, which latter we bought in lead carboys. We had a formula for this mixing operation but our aluminum fluoride never seemed to come out right. I watched Mike one day and discovered that he was not weighing the hydrofluoric acid. When I asked him why he was not weighing it, he said that it was not necessary to weigh it for he had discovered that there was a pound for every gurgle and a gurgle for every pound.

"I think about the greatest cross that Mr. Hall and I had to bear was working out a scheme which was invented by Professor J. W. Langley. It seems that Captain Hunt had met Mr. Langley and explained to him about the pots fuming and Mr. Langley invented the scheme of making a paste of alumina and hydrofluoric acid which Mr. Hall or I would put into the pots and, having poked it underneath, would turn and run to get away from the explosion and particularly the gas which frequently made the blood come to our noses. One day Captain Hunt and several other people came out to the plant and wanted to see us do that job. When they saw what it involved, they told us never to do it again.

116

"I remember the time when Jack Williams, owner of the Springfield Foundry, came across the street to tell me that he considered George Clapp one of the greatest financiers in the United States. I agreed with him in this, but I naturally asked him why he so regarded Mr. Clapp. Jack said that we owed the Springfield Foundry some money for castings and Mr. Clapp had just told him he was very sorry he could not pay because he had run out of checks. I might say that such excuses for not paying our bills was a rather common sort of thing in those days, but not everyone took it as pleasantly and as philosophically as Jack Williams."

An important event in pot-room management took place on Sunday, September 29, 1889, when Charles Bradley reported for work at the Smallman Street plant. Bradley started on one of those bad days. The pots were acting up, and the building was full of fumes. Davis doubted whether his new man would last more than a day. At its close, he managed a seemingly casual remark: "You know, Charley, we don't have it this bad all the time!" To this observation Charley replied, "Do you think this is bad? Did you ever lie down on your side and pick coal over your head with a pickax for 12 hours?"

Working the pots was a tough hard job, but Charley Bradley learned their idiosyncrasies and became a competent foreman that Hall and Davis could rely on. He helped manage company pot rooms until his retirement some 34 years later.

Even though Hall did not have to live near the works, his almost constant attendance necessitated finding convenient places to eat. Indigestion and seemingly endless fatigue were endured without complaint as part of the price for achievement. In January of '89, Charles answered Julia's query regarding his boarding place:

"I get part of my meals at a place not far from my room

117

in East Liberty. It is quite a good place, as good as I have found in Pittsburgh certainly for the price. I average about one meal a day there. The rest I have to get near our works or in the city. I have been trying to find a good place near our works for a long time but have not succeeded. I go to several places and I think it would nearly make you sick to go into one. In one place I used to sit facing the door to avoid the dirty, disagreeable sights at the other end of the room . . . If I have written you a very stupid letter you must remember that the way I have been doing—eating, sleeping and working, principally the last—is not calculated to make one fit to write any better."

And a month later Hall wrote the folks in Oberlin:

"I have given up getting my meals around our place and my digestion is much better with good reason. I get a good breakfast at the East End then wait till five or six o'clock and go to the city and get a good square dinner at some good restaurant. Then I go back to the works and stay there till 8 or 9 o'clock. This has been the program the past week or two. Tonight I commence working nights again."

Each Sunday brought Charles face to face with two duties, usually pleasurable but not always compatible with the inexorable requirements of his aluminum process. In his letters to Julia, Charles occasionally explains his failure to write by the necessity of attending Satan's Church which was his whimsical Sunday appellation for the aluminum works on Smallman Street. In his own words:

"I have to go to Satan's Church pretty often Sundays and don't have time to write letters or do anything else. We cannot stop our engines, dynamos and pots Sunday, as it would require till about the middle of the week to start again."

From time to time Hall enjoyed Sunday dinner with the Hunts. These red-letter days started him thinking of the time when he would have an establishment of his own, with a charming hostess to grace his table:

"I have been to his (Captain Hunt's) house to dinner today and had a very good dinner, better than I have had before in a long time. I am tired of boarding and if I ever get rich am going to have an establishment of my own."

The company's second full year of aluminum manufacture started in January, 1890, with the Board of Directors raising Hall's salary to one hundred and twenty-five dollars per month. This was a welcome move, for the company's stock was not yet on a dividend-paying basis. Then Hall received another surprise when he was instructed to prepare to sail for Europe at once, not later than January 18. He was to look after the "working" of his foreign patents to prevent their lapsing.

Also in January, Hall sold sixty shares of his stock to secure some ready cash. This sale brought into the company's family of shareholders, a man who was to prove a lifelong friend and staunch supporter of the company. Andrew W. Mellon paid Hall six thousand dollars for these shares, his first stock in The Pittsburgh Reduction Company.

119

9

. . . *Josie was the woman*

JOSEPHINE LUCRETIA CODY, the idol of fond parents, stemmed from a prominent Cleveland family of comfortable means. One relative, Colonel W. F. (Buffalo Bill) Cody, had helped make the family name well known both as soldier and actor. Just about the time that Buffalo Bill started his famous Wild West Show, young Charlie Hall was casting romantic glances at Josephine on the Oberlin campus. She was an attractive brunette with large brown eyes, clear complexion and well-rounded figure. Always modishly attired and gifted with poise and friendly manner, Josephine was a popular member of the Class of '85.

In his dreams, Josie was the woman Charlie had chosen to grace the home he was planning for the day when he would be a rich inventor. There were visions of Charlie and Josie playing duets on a fine new piano, and Charlie and Josie entertaining their friends at dinner. Mr. and Mrs. Charles Martin

122

Hall would be seen at the opera and he would be pointed out as the man who had discovered cheap aluminum. Together they would travel abroad—to England, Europe and the Orient. But it was still only a dream with no evidence of early fruition. Would Josephine wait?

After graduation, Josephine returned to her home in Cleveland and Charles went back to his experiments. The flame of their affection was not burning brightly but the spark was still there. Josephine's mother, maternally ambitious, decided to broaden her education and widen her group of friends with a year or so at an eastern college. She was soon busy collecting her wardrobe and packing for the trip East. Dressed in her traveling costume, she appeared to have just stepped from a page in *Godey's Lady's Book*. On her arrival in Boston, Josephine enrolled in Wellesley College for a year of graduate study.

At home again the following summer, this ambitious young lady continued the study of music begun at the Oberlin Conservatory the year before entering college. With the experience gained in travel and study, Josephine developed a mature and charming personality with a natural interest in people, an interest which eventually developed into an absorbing participation in civic activities.

For several years Charles's courting had to be carried on by correspondence and during occasional trips to Cleveland. Tangible clues to the progress of the romance are first found in his letters to his family. Bashful in writing about love, Charles assumed a very casual manner in telling his family how the affair was progressing. In January of '89, he confided to Louie, his youngest sister:

"My girl has not written to me lately (her mother has

123

gone to Mexico and that must be the reason) so I don't have to write to her. Besides I don't have to work tonight as I did last Sunday night and take the day for sleeping. So you see I have time to write to you and it is my first opportunity since receiving your letter."

A month later, the dynamo in the Smallman Street aluminum works burned out and, while waiting for Westinghouse to supply a new armature, Charles made a hurried trip to Cleveland for a visit with Josephine. After his return to Pittsburgh, he wrote Julia about the trip and about a gay supper party he attended where he played whist and "had a very pleasant time." Old college friends were there and, after the party, he rode back to the city in a street car with classmates of his, Homer Johnson and his wife. Only as an afterthought did he tell Julia, "Last Sunday I went with Miss Cody to visit the Bethlehem Sunday School where she teaches." No mention was made of other visits with Josephine, yet events suggest that they were reaching an understanding.

If Charles was waiting for his aluminum process to demonstrate itself before pressing Josephine for an answer, that time was close at hand. The company was planning an extension to its Smallman Street works, and considering ways and means of securing additional capital for its operations. The future looked bright even though the company always seemed short of cash.

Soon it was spring and the miracle happened. Charlie and Josie became engaged. Josie told her mother, and Charles wrote his family. Their teen-age romance appeared at last, after more than five years' vicissitudes, to be the prelude to marriage. Charles acknowledged his family's good wishes in his Sunday letter of May 26, 1889:

124

"Your congratulations were very pleasant and I thank you and the others for them. I have a way of leaving the most important things till the last, but that doesn't prove that I consider them least.

The secrecy with which Charles surrounded his activities in business and invention extended to his personal affairs. He was reticent in telling his family about his interest in Josephine. She was a good Sunday School teacher and took a great interest in missionary work, he said, but there is no indication that he told them what a lovely girl was Josie, how companionable and what a help she was going to be in his career as an inventor. It is quite possible that he was likewise reticent and shy with Josephine. Even though Josie listened attentively to the wonders of aluminum, she was hungry to be told that her silken tresses shone with a glint of gold, that her beautiful brown eyes thrilled him through and through. The metallurgy of aluminum was no substitute for the alchemy of love. Even while rejoicing over his newly accepted love, Charles sounded a note of caution on its permanency:

"I had a letter from the young lady at 1707 Broadway Cleveland this afternoon in which she said that Miss Anna Peck and John Peck were calling upon her last week and mentioned the fact that Mr. Stimson was in Oberlin and Miss Peck said he would probably be out to see her, that is see Miss Peck. Finding that Miss Cody knew him, she said that she would tell Mr. Stimson where she lived. You can tell my brother-in-law (Martin Luther Stimson—a missionary) of this. I think he would find it pleasant to call. Miss Cody is much more active and interested in missionary work and missions than a good many other people. You asked how long I had been 'engaged.' Only a short time.

125

Josephine Lucretia Cody

The young lady said she had only told her mother and did not care to tell anyone else at present. Perhaps she wants to see if it will last. You can govern yourself by the same plan. I have given you her address, 1707 Broadway and should be glad to have you write if you wish to.

Your aff. brother,

C. M. H."

126

Julia's collection of her brother's letters is without even a scribbled note from June 1889 to February 1891. These were important and busy months in Charles's life. His aluminum process was working so well that the company was recapitalized as a million-dollar corporation, and he was sent to England on a business trip. After business came pleasure and Charles was fascinated by the historic spots he visited on short excursions through England, Scotland and Wales. Later he found time for more extended trips on the continent. Travel he found both exciting and diverting, and diversion he needed, for his engagement to Josephine was languishing if not ended.

Charles was back in Pittsburgh by November, and found many matters requiring his attention. In June of '91 he took time to query Julia: "Please write and tell me when is Commencement and what are the attractions. My class holds a reunion this year. On some accounts I should like to be present."

Could it be that some lingering hope pictured Josephine as one of the attractions? A week later Charles again brought up the subject: "Please write me about Commencement. I understand Miss Cody is to be there. What are the attractions in the way of concerts or other doings?"

John C. Sherman, the senator from Ohio, was the speaker at Oberlin's 1891 graduation exercises. In his address to the hopeful and aspiring young graduates, the senator referred to his Congressional activities in the previous year in securing the passage of the Sherman Anti-Trust Law. Then, in best commencement style, he took a look at the Big Things yet to be accomplished, and wished that he was one of the graduates stepping out into a world of opportunity just waiting to be conquered. Little did the senator realize what penalties the courts of future years were going to read into his law, if only

127

one succeeded too well; and Charles could not have anticipated the shocks which the Sherman Anti-Trust law was going to give his aluminum company in future years. At the moment his mind was too preoccupied with thoughts of Josephine to pay much attention to the senator.

Josephine went abroad in 1892 for a year of music study in Germany. Not long after her return, on December 27, 1893, she married an attorney and went to live in Chicago. A group picture taken at Class reunion in 1903 shows Josephine in the front row sitting on the grass beside a college building. Standing in the rear row is Charles, stealing a wistful glance at Josie's smiling profile.

This was the one dream that never came true. Hall never married. In time, he acquired a home in Niagara Falls, but there was almost more care than pleasure in the acquisition. Wedded to aluminum, he sought the solace of music to fill the emptiness of his home.

10

*. . . sailed for England,
as planned*

FOREIGN PATENTS on Hall's aluminum process were a
matter of both hope and concern to the company. The directors *hoped* that the patents could be sold to provide needed
capital for the company's expansion in America. They were
concerned lest Héroult and others, stimulated by the success
of the Hall process, would be the first to seize opportunity in
England and on the continent. Charles explained the situation
to Julia in his Sunday letters starting February 3 in '89:

"Our patents which we care particularly about, 6 of them
in all, are allowed in this country . . . the lawyers are now
going ahead on the foreign patents. This company and
enterprise is now bound to go ahead. If it finally fails it will
be in the commercial point of view as the Cowles Co. has
failed after years of work and piles of money have been
spent. Captain Hunt told me Friday that we had made

away with $18,000 already. It looks incredible and I think he is mistaken, but it is a good deal. He told me something else, that there was plenty more money to go into the enterprise, though they would like a little better showing in results (which I think they will get very soon)."

A week later, Charles had more news for Julia:

"During the last week I have been helping our lawyer get his foreign patent applications in shape. Wednesday I went to see the Austrian, Norwegian, Swedish and Italian consuls to fix up some papers for patents in each country and in all the European countries except Turkey, Spain and Portugal. In six weeks the applications will be filed and our patents (United States) issued here either on the 19th or 26th of March. After that you are at liberty to tell people I am in Pittsburgh and we don't care a darn for the Cowles' or anyone else. . . . Another interesting fact is that Hunt already has his ticket engaged to go to Europe about May or June, principally on business connected with disposing of or utilizing these patents. The scheme is to raise as much ready money from them as possible for works in the United States."

Captain Hunt and Hall were doing some wishful thinking about the foreign patents for on May 5 Charles wrote Julia:

"The company said they would sell our Luxemburg patents for a quarter of a million as a joke, partly. Hunt says he hopes to get a million for them all and possibly more. He is going to work it for all it is worth. He leaves three weeks from yesterday . . . (and on May 26). You asked about our foreign patents. Only one has been secured as yet—the one of Luxemburg. The rest are applied for in all countries except Spain, Portugal and Turkey. The only countries where a patent is not issued as a matter of course on application being made are England and Germany. In all other countries you can get a patent on any application and then defend it if it is good for anything afterwards. There is no special reason to fear trouble in England and Germany. The applications were filed April 2 and in the natural course of events the patents will issue in the month of June unless possibly we have trouble in the two countries named. So you see there is no doubt of Hunt's having something to sell. He is going to spend the first month in looking around and not open negotiations directly till the patents issue.

"I suppose Captain Hunt is feeding the fishes about this time. He sailed yesterday."

Julia has crossed out with ink the suggestion of *mal de mer*. Apparently she did not approve of Charles's unsympathetic reference to the captain's seamanship.

The trip was a memorable one for the Hunts since the captain was accompanied by his wife and eight-year-old son. They took part in what the program called a "Visit of American Engineers to the United Kingdom." Hunt was a prominent member of the group for he was vice-president of the American Institute of Mining Engineers and also a member of the American Society of Civil Engineers and the Iron and Steel Institute of Great Britain. The meetings gave Captain Hunt excellent opportunities to meet prominent engineers and leaders of industry. Good background was thus obtained for the aluminum project to be negotiated later. Trips through historic England and France were also a treat for Mrs. Hunt and young Roy.

By the middle of August, Captain Hunt was able to inform his directors in Pittsburgh that he had completed the preliminary arrangements for the formation of the Metal Reduction Company Syndicate Ltd. of London, England. The Syndicate was to furnish £10,000 in cash to erect a small aluminum plant in England. If a trial run of six months was deemed successful, the plan contemplated the organization of a LARGE company with capital of £5,000,000 sterling. The Pittsburgh Reduction Company would then receive generous amounts of cash and stock for its patents. By the end of September, the details of the syndicate organization had been perfected and Captain Hunt and his family were ready for the journey home.

Captain Hunt attended the directors' meeting in Pittsburgh on October 16 and was officially thanked for his successful conduct of the British negotiations. He reported that a group of thirteen London citizens, bankers, brokers, merchants and others—had subscribed £9,000 and he had put The Pittsburgh Reduction Company down for £2,000 sterling. The directors were still in an expansive mood on October 22 when they elected Chas. M. Hall to the Board. Charles had not only shown that he could build and operate an aluminum plant but that he also could be a good business adviser.

The company's secretary, W. S. Sample, was soon dispatched to England to get the project started. Apparently Hall had doubts as to Sample's engineering talents for he made the wry comment, "He goes as an 'expert' and manager. Why he is called expert I am unable to determine. . . . I am expected to go over in a few weeks and show the 'expert' how to run things." Hall sailed for England in January, as planned.

Construction of the aluminum works was undertaken at Patricroft near Manchester. This project took most of Hall's time for several months after his arrival in England in January. His habitual long working hours earned for him the respect and interest of the plant's workers. They even tried to find him a wife. This is the story Hall spun for Julia:

"Most of the old employees . . . are more interesting, I think, than a similar crowd in Pittsburgh would be. There is a funny story about old 'Tom,' one of the firemen. Since coming to our works he married a new young wife who used to bring his supper to him and spend the evening keeping him company (Tom had to take care of the boilers). There was another young woman who had wanted to marry him, and to pacify her he told her about me, that I was an American and was going to return pretty soon, and perhaps would like to take a wife home with me. So she came around to the works to see me one evening when I wasn't there. When she found out Tom had fooled her, she knocked him down and Stevens had to get some of the men and put her out of the yard."

While at Manchester, short trips through the countryside and to nearby historic spots were taken as opportunity offered, but when the pressure of work lifted, Hall was able to travel more widely. From London, he wrote his classmates at Oberlin:

"The last month I have spent in London and on the continent at Brussels and Paris. It is very good fun to be in London. I have been here two weeks now; have been to the Tower, Westminster Abbey and St. Paul's: have heard Canon Farrar, Henry Irving, Miss Terry, Mrs. Langtry and Mr. Spurgeon. Yesterday I heard some very good speaking in the House of Commons, where I am going again this evening. The other day I saw a procession of ladies from the Queen's Drawing Room. It was a gay sight. I quite agree with a friend of mine who says that London is the grandest town on earth."

After his return from England, his European trip again formed the subject of his class letter for 1891:

"A year ago I wrote you from England. Although in Europe for other reasons, I enjoyed my stay there perhaps as much as though I had gone solely for a pleasure trip. Most of the time I spent in England, living in Eccles, a suburb of Manchester. I enjoyed my life there; I lived in 'apartments' like the famous Mr. Pickwick—the English style, which is much better than boarding, much more independent and more homelike.

"I visited a good many places in England, among them Chester, with its old Roman and Saxon walls, and Eaton Hall, the splendid home of the duke of Westminster. I took a good many bicycle trips through Cheshire and Derbyshire and North Wales. I saw many most lovely spots in Wales, places where Tennyson might have written the lines,

'The splendor falls on castle walls, etc.'

"It was Whit week that I spent in Wales with some English friends. Perhaps some of the theologically inclined of you know what Whit week is. I don't, but it is a week when all England takes a holiday. The English take more holidays than Americans, and people above the laboring class there take life easier than we do.

"Late in the summer I went to Edinburgh, the Trossachs and the Scotch lakes, and after that to the Isle of Man, where the ocean is the bluest and clearest I ever saw. There I happened to see the yacht 'Sunbeam.'

135

Charles Martin Hall at age of thirty-three

"The month of August found me in London and from there I went to Vienna, where I spent three weeks. Vienna is truly a splendid city, and they do things royally there for the entertainment of strangers. There is the finest street in the world, and the group of buildings on it are not equalled anywhere. There, too, is the finest opera and the most costly and magnificent theatre in the world.

136

"After Vienna I visited southern Austria, where I had my first glimpse of the snow-covered Alps; also the Tyrol and Bavaria. On the morning of Sunday, the 14th of September, I was summoned by the booming of a cannon to the opening of the 'Passion' play at the theatre in Oberammergau. I won't attempt, what has been done so often, to describe this 'Passion' play. It was far better and stronger than I had anticipated and worthy of the best that has been said about it.

"While at Oberammergau, I visited Linderhof, one of crazy King Ludwig's palaces. I had already visited that at Herrenschirmsee, where single curtains were shown worth $80,000. On the way back to Munich, from Oberammergau, I could see the great snow-covered Bavarian Alps. I had intended to visit Switzerland and attempt a little mountain climbing there, but I had to give that up for lack of time.

"The last of September I returned to England, and after a few days spent in wandering about Warwick county where are Kenilworth Castle, Warwick Castle and Stratford-on-Avon, and a few days in London and at Eccles, I sailed for home on the 15th of October on the newest of the ocean greyhounds, the *Majestic,* and was glad to see America once more."

Charles returned home with a feeling of achievement. The Patricroft plant had started making aluminum in July, and he was elated with his first experience at world travel. But the high hopes for profit from foreign patents were a mirage, and with the months and years were due to fade and pass. However, success in America would more than compensate for this disappointment.

11

. . . working again on
the battery

REFRESHED from travel abroad, Charles's mind began to churn with invention as soon as he was back in Pittsburgh. Even though the aluminum business had serious problems demanding attention, the call of the laboratory was insistent.

Charles had developed the practice of recording in a notebook, various bits of chemical lore he noted in his reading, but, more particularly, ideas of an inventive nature which flashed through his fertile mind. These ideas might be aids to the solution of an old problem with which he had been struggling for months or years, or might suggest new projects which looked profitable. Even in the midst of an absorbing interest in aluminum, Charles's mind kept turning to other subjects. Invention was at times a hobby that brought relaxation from worrisome commercial and technical difficulties.

Julia preserved among her brother's letters and papers, copies of several pages from one of these notebooks. The first three entries are dated February 14, 1888, a day when Hall was working at Lockport, trying to convince the Cowles brothers that he had a practical process for producing pure aluminum. The six-month option he had given Cowles' had just expired on January 26 without any indication that it would be exercised, and Hall was duly disappointed. These first notebook entries suggest a renewed interest in filaments for the Edison electric lamp. Perhaps Hall was hoping to make other inventions which could bring cash to the rescue of his first love, aluminum. Other ideas include testing the effect of alloying chromium, titanium or tungsten with aluminum bronze and the addition of chromium and titanium to pure aluminum.

Then there is a cryptic note dated April 30, 1888, which says:

> *"Learned today that zinc distills but little above its melting point in a vacuum."*

Charles was so secretive about his projects that frequently he refused to let his own private notebook know what was passing through his mind when he wrote therein. This is a case in point. After the April 30 entry, he later put this note:

> "(Very important, Jan. 8 '90)"

Eventually, he told Julia that he was working again on the battery in which he became interested in the summer of 1884. Hall now had a double interest in completing this invention, for it was his secret hope that he might, with this new type of battery, secure cheap electricity for the production of aluminum.

Making a suitable hollow and porous electrode for his battery was the starting point for work in January, 1891. Hall hoped that a gaseous fuel such as water gas, introduced into the hollow electrode, would flow through the porous walls and be oxidized (burned electrochemically) at the outer surface in contact with the electrolyte. This electrochemical reaction should produce an electric current, and with more than double the efficiency obtained by burning the fuel under a boiler to generate steam to turn a dynamo.

Buckley, a machinist and handy man at the Smallman Street plant, assisted Hall in making porous tubes for his battery. Hall was alternately elated and disappointed with the progress made. On February 1, he wrote Julia:

"This letter I think you better preserve and also the enclosed wires or tubes with it. You will notice that these wires are really tubes with an aluminum core. It is only necessary to soak them a few days or perhaps less in hydrochloric or hydrofluoric acid to remove the aluminum and leave them hollow all the way through. I made a tube that way last week—put it to soak the week before, and now have 30 or 40, 6-inch lengths of about the size that I send you, in the acid dissolving out the aluminum.

"This seems to be the way to make the tubes that I want, and I believe that it will make perfect ones of any size and thickness of wall wanted. These that I send you are 1/16 inch in outside diameter with a wall about .015 inch thick. They are drawn down from a cylinder ¾ inch in diameter, about 8 inches long, which was drilled on the lathe and a ⅜ inch aluminum rod put in the center. I tried using iron in the center, but it did not work as well as the aluminum does.

"I have tubes enough now to make a battery, that is, a small one. They are about of the right composition, that is, the old alloy that you know about, and all that is needed is to take the aluminum out, and then the zinc, of which they contain about 40 to 45%, by heating in a vacuum, and I think I shall be very near then to getting what I want. See —"

The company's legal troubles with the Cowles Company took so much of Hall's time that little was accomplished on the battery in the following weeks. On April 2, he wrote:

"I have done so little work on the battery lately that I am anxious to get at that as soon as this preliminary hearing is finished and before something else comes up to take my time. I have been able to do almost nothing for two weeks, except that Mr. Buckley is gradually getting materials and apparatus into shape so that something decisive may be accomplished soon. Please write me how things are at home and whether there is any object beyond a visit in my coming."

On May 10:

"The work on the battery still drags along. I tell Buckley that I am willing to keep at it a year, provided I don't succeed as I wish sooner. It is a kind of work where you must expect to plod along week after week and be satisfied if you have gained anything in months. I have gained a good deal lately, I think.

"Two weeks ago the problem was to make the tubes porous without burning and spoiling them. I have found a way, which, if not perfect, is a great advance on what I had at first. It is possible that I have everything needed now— and only have to go ahead and make a battery—but I can't tell."

143

Hall planned to use an acid electrolyte in his battery, and this necessitated making the electrodes from an acid-resistant alloy. On May 24, he wrote Julia:

"I have had bad luck all the week with the battery and all the week before—the way of it is this. You know I had found a metal that would resist the corrosion of acid indefinitely. I found that out seven years ago. Since working here I have made a metal alloy containing exactly the same elements but have made it in a different way from what I made the alloy in my old experiments. Made the new way it is very ductile. I find that made in the new way it is not nearly so good to resist the acid, in fact, not good enough, and that the metal made in the old way (the elements are the same but exist in different state evidently) is brittle, or at least not ductile. It is evidently just on the border between ductility and nonductility, and to make the tubes the metal must be ductile. I have made up specimen after specimen, forged it out hot, had Buckley turn it up on the lathe and make a tube—to be drawn smaller—and then the second or the fourth or the sixth hole in the die plate it would crack. Yesterday I got a piece that seemed particularly ductile and malleable, but the second hole in the draw plate cracked it all to pieces. So I am up a stump. If I can overcome this difficulty, I will have a chance of doing something."

June 7, '91:

"The battery experiments have been in the dumps too—and several days ago I almost made up my mind that what I needed to obtain for success required the fulfillment of a set of conditions which was impossible."

144

Although Hall displayed ingenuity in constructing a hollow and porous electrode, he never realized that obtaining a workable electrolyte for his battery was a more difficult problem to solve than that of the electrodes. Although a good experimenter, he was not a sufficiently profound scientist to understand the electrochemical dilemma which balked success. Nevertheless, whenever new ideas and opportunity presented themselves, he renewed his attack on the battery project.

The next week Charles wrote Julia about an episode which must have reminded her of the days when her brother first started experimenting in the cupola of the family home on East College Street. In his current investigation the result was not a fire, but the unexpected chemical reaction products landed on the ceiling of the plant at Smallman Street:

"Yesterday I had a real annoying accident that disturbed my equanimity. I was working with some stuff that explodes on contact with water—distilling it out of a flask into a bottle, and the bottle was in a pail of water to keep it cool and condense the vapor that distilled over. In the first place the outlet tube got stopped up and the flask blew the bottom out, but that didn't do any particular harm except that it tipped over the glass bottle in the pail of water and let the water into it. I started to straighten it up and it exploded with a tremendous bang and blew the thick glass bottle all to pieces. I got my hands cut some but not seriously. The force of the explosion was mostly spent in blowing the pail of water around the room. If the thing had happened a little differently I might have been half killed—as it was I wasn't hurt to amount to anything. . . . You see I have very little to write."

When work on the battery failed to make progress, Hall

turned to another field of invention which he had started to cultivate while in college. Edison's electric lamp was still something of a novelty, and Hall rightly sensed that it offered further rewards for inventive effort. His old attempt to make a tungsten filament during college days had failed. He now turned to other materials, as related to Julia:

"I have started to try some experiments (at the same time keeping on with the battery) on my new electric lamp scheme. I have tried to start on that before this winter— but couldn't make the stuff I wanted to work with. Saturday I succeeded in making a lot of it. This electric light scheme is far simpler than the other and if it amounts to anything might really be worth almost as much."

The nature of the "stuff" which he had succeeded in making was kept secret, even from Julia, but entries in his laboratory notebook suggest that he had been speculating for some time on the possibility of making filaments through the use of aluminum boride, boron nitride or boron. Just how he intended to use these refractory materials was not disclosed. Without a doubt, ideas for electric lamp filaments kept buzzing in Hall's head for many years but nothing tangible came of them. Arthur Davis has said:

"While Hall was not patient, he was what you might really call persistent. He had a funny way of always going back to things. I have seen him playing chess many times, and sometimes when it wouldn't go right he would get mad and throw the whole thing over, but in half an hour he would go back and set it all up again and work the whole thing out. And that is the way he was with everything. He would work on a certain thing until he would get up against what seemed like a dead wall and then he would quit, and he thought he had quit for good, but he would always go back at it until he finally worked it out."

The Pittsburgh Reduction Company was now in its third year and these were lean years, financially speaking. Both Hall and the company were forced to frugal living since earnings in the form of dividends had not yet made their appearance. Captain Hunt served as president of the company without salary. However, after the first year's operations, the Board of Directors voted themselves and the treasurer a "remuneration of $260 each" for their services. Beginning January 1890, the remuneration was changed to five dollars per meeting, "the same to be paid at the adjournment of the meeting." At the same meeting, the Finance Committee was authorized to "prepare a statement of the financial credit of the company for Dunn and Bradstreet." On that occasion the Board of Directors also resolved "that the treasurer be instructed to have a telephone put in at the works as soon as the office is finished." It may be that an obliging neighbor in the steel business was getting tired of having Hall and Davis running over to use their telephone.

Although the business sun shone occasionally, there were still blue Mondays for Hall, as he confessed to Julia:

"I have had a fit of discouragement pretty much all the week on business matters. I have been afraid the aluminum business was going to the d——l. We need more money and can't get it—or haven't got it yet. Today, however, I feel much better. I have been to see Captain Hunt this afternoon. He is in good spirits apparently."

In addition to his concern about the technical operation of the process, Hall's positions as vice-president and as a director of the company were rapidly contributing to his education in

147

the techniques of business. He was also learning about the hazards of free enterprise in the exacting School of Experience. In his Sunday letter of May 3, Charles paid his respects to the economic views of Dr. Lyman Abbott. Dr. Abbott, who had succeeded Henry Ward Beecher at the Plymouth Congregational Church in Brooklyn, was collecting audiences by the controversial theories on political economy which he was advancing as a minister, lecturer and editor. Hall's opinions are of interest not only as a chapter in the education of an inventor, but also for the contrast between the views of the practitioner and the theorist:

"I have seen Dr. Lyman Abbott and have known something of his ideas on Political Economy. . . . Abbott wants the workmen in a mill to control the mill and the business. I think I have had a great deal more to do with workmen than Dr. Abbott has. Even my man Buckley laughs at such an idea. Buckley is a superior sort of workman. He is a machinist and has the ability to 'use tools,' as Abbott put it, but the mechanical skill and ability to use tools is one thing and the ability to combine his work with that of others and adapt it all to a valuable and profitable purpose is quite another—and that Buckley has not got. He can earn the most and really do the most good for himself and society when he does just what other people tell him.

"There isn't a man about our works whom I believe would think that he was competent or would care to take the responsibility of running the place, to say nothing of managing the business. I have seen cases where in just using the 'tools,' dynamos, etc., that they are supposed to have ability to use, they are as helpless as infants. They haven't got the knowledge or quickness or the *nerve* to meet an

148

emergency. . . . Abbott shows his lack of information in saying that one man practically controls electricity in this country. He probably is one of those people who think that Edison discovered electricity and that Edison and electricity are convertible terms.

"Abbott wants the government to own the gold mines— I suppose he means only the successful and valuable ones, and that those are to belong to the government when found. . . . If the government is going to confiscate for a 'reward' the good ones as soon as proved good, people will stop risking their time and money in hunting for gold mines and developing them. It is the same way, to a greater or less extent, with coal mines, railroad enterprises, manufacturing industries and inventions. The greater part of such enter-prises fail, or at least are unproductive for a long period. It takes nerve and perseverance and foresight, and even then people go into these sort of things knowing that the chances are against them. . . .

"Mr. Abbott makes the mistake at the outset, as most of his ilk do, of supposing that the wealth of the country depends upon its natural resources and the laboring or muscle-power, as you might call it, of the people. . . . The wealth of this country and of this time depends far more and has been multiplied many fold by the mind-power rather than the labor-power, and particularly the freedom and incentive which everyone has to use his mind to do things better than his neighbors and better than has been done before. The same thing is true of the wealth of other countries, like England. Now Mr. Abbott wants to destroy both the freedom and the incentive and to place the control of industry in the hands of the people who haven't contrib-uted the essential thing to develop it and haven't the ability to preserve it. . . . I have written the above more from a desire to put in shape my own ideas on the subject than because I suppose they will interest you."

Charles had firsthand opportunities for learning some of labor's contributions to enterprise, when working with his "man Buckley," making metal tubes for the battery. With pride of accomplishment he wrote Julia:

"I have worked like a blacksmith—hammering ingots all day—but am none the worse for it. Buckley and I organize ourselves into a rolling mill on occasions—every day nowadays, and I am getting up a lot of muscle in my arms. Buckley thinks if I came to it, I could earn as much as a dollar and a half a day swinging a sledge hammer.

Your aff. brother

C. M. Hall"

In spite of economic problems, The Pittsburgh Reduction Company was slowly gaining momentum. Greater metal capacity seemed called for and the Smallman Street plant was enlarged. By September 1890, metal production had been increased to about 5,000 pounds a month and this figure was soon doubled. By March, there was so much metal on hand that a waiting policy was adopted. Soon after, a very attractive offer was made to the company. Hall explained the plan to his sister in his letter of May 10:

"Dear Julia:

"I received your letter as usual last week and came near not writing today at all. There is not much to write about, as it is.

"Last Thursday I went to the country for the afternoon, 17 miles up the Allegheny River beyond Verona and Parnassus, to a new proposed town, Kensington, where we are offered free land, cheap coal, and $10,000 cash to move our works, provided we will accept the offer this week. I think very likely the offer will be accepted. The $10,000 will just about pay the cost of moving, perhaps a little more. The place is a very good one for our purpose. We can get coal there for about 30 or 40 cents a ton. We have got to use coal anyway, as the natural gas is too expensive. We can have all the land we want for nothing; no taxes or rent. Altogether we could save probably $15,000 or $20,000 a year there—perhaps not so much but a good deal over the present manufacturing expenses in Pittsburgh and have plenty of room to enlarge. The proposed Scranton deal, by which we were to sell $100,000 stock and move to Scranton, has fizzled, at least that is what I think, though we haven't heard definitely either way."

The Kensington offer proved most attractive and was accepted. The town was renamed New Kensington. Construction of a new plant was soon underway and it was making aluminum by November.

Success at the Smallman Street works was the result of teamwork, and five members of the company thought that Mr. Davis deserved special recognition and should be made a shareholder. On March 11, 1891, "In consideration of the efficient services of Mr. Arthur V. Davis, as superintendent of The Pittsburgh Reduction Company, and as a special mark of esteem," they presented him with twenty-three shares of the company's stock. Ten of these shares were the gift of Charles M. Hall. This was significant recognition for, as the years passed, Mr. Davis carried more and more managerial responsibility.

The pioneer works on Smallman Street left a proud record. Before production was stopped in March of 1891, the little works had produced a total of 87,739 pounds of aluminum. During the last month, production in the enlarged pot room set a new monthly record for the infant industry of 12,837 pounds of aluminum. By then, the company's inventory was so large that production was not resumed until November at New Kensington. The site of the Smallman Street works is now marked by an aluminum tablet which proclaims:

THIS TABLET MARKS THE
BIRTHPLACE OF THE ALUMINUM
INDUSTRY IN THE
UNITED STATES
ON THE SITE OF THIS BUILDING
THE PITTSBURGH REDUCTION COMPANY,
NOW ALUMINUM COMPANY OF AMERICA,
LATE IN NOVEMBER 1888, PRODUCED
THE FIRST COMMERCIAL RUN OF ALUMINUM
BY THE HALL ELECTROLYTIC PROCESS.

———————

ERECTED BY
THE HISTORICAL SOCIETY OF
WESTERN PENNSYLVANIA
NOVEMBER 1938

12

. . . Judge Taft upheld the Hall patent

RUMORS had been reaching Hall for some time that the Cowles people were going to make trouble for Hall and The Pittsburgh Reduction Company. One story was that the Cowles Company would sue for infringement of their patents. They were asserting that they had a monopoly on the use of electricity for smelting aluminum ores, a fantastic claim indeed. Other information brought to Hall told of financial difficulties harassing the Cowles Electric Smelting and Aluminum Company. Just as Hall and Cole had figured, the pure aluminum from the Hall process was providing competition which the Cowles alloy process could not meet.

Captain Hunt had taken an ingot of The Pittsburgh Reduction Company's first aluminum to New York to sell at $5 a pound. The price was soon set at $4 a pound for No. 1 metal. During the year of '89 the price gradually drifted downward, $3.00, then $2.50, and finally $2.00 in lots of one thousand pounds and over. By fall, one customer purchased some metal at $1.50 a pound. In a good month, production amounted to about 1,500 pounds a month and the mill cost was about one dollar a pound. By next spring, mill costs had dropped below the dollar figure. Hall wrote Cole:

"The mention of $2 in 1,000-pound lots didn't seem to interest anyone. I know a good many people look at it as a big guy, and they have reason to do so, as they know that the total consumption of aluminum in the U. S. has hardly been 1,000 pounds a year. People have said we didn't have 1,000 pounds. They were wrong but they might have said, that so far as the users of aluminum were concerned, practically no one wanted 1,000 pounds."

Although the Cowles Company did not make pure aluminum prior to 1891, and could not make it by their electrothermic alloy process, they sold some aluminum purchased from The Pittsburgh Reduction Company and some purchased from the Castner people in Europe. They also showed an interest in joining forces with Hall's company. In June of 1890, The Pittsburgh Reduction Company received a telegram from Eugene Cowles asking that a representative be sent to Montreal to discuss combining and working the Canadian patents of the two companies. George Clapp made the trip. According to his testimony:

"In answer to this telegram, I went to Montreal, being with Mr. Cowles on the 30th of June and the 2nd of July. At these conversations I was strongly urged to use every effort to bring about a consolidation of the Canadian patents of the two companies, and the consolidation of the U. S. patents as well was incidentally brought up in the course of these meetings by Mr. Cowles. During several visits of Mr. Alfred Cowles to Pitts-

155

burgh, prior to going to Europe in 1890, this subject was also frequently mentioned by Mr. Cowles."

Mr. Clapp was asked whether the suggestion of Mr. Cowles was accepted by The Pittsburgh Reduction Company, and he answered: "It was not."

The Cowles Company, hard pressed financially, proceeded to pirate Hall's electrolytic process. Although they knew the general plan of Hall's process, they were not familiar with the construction and operation of the reduction pots. Appropriating this information seemed to be a quicker and cheaper procedure than making the development themselves, so the Cowles Company hired one of The Pittsburgh Reduction Company's pot-room operators, John C. Hobbs.

Hobbs had been employed by The Pittsburgh Reduction Company from January, 1889 to December 10, 1890, the day he left for Lockport. Although not technically trained, Hobbs could tell the Cowles people quite well how to set up a pot room and operate it the way he had been taught by Hall and Davis.

By the second week in January, the Cowles Company was making pure aluminum and advertising the fact they had pure aluminum for sale.

Hall and his associates were not taken by surprise; they assumed that Cowles had hired Hobbs for the purpose of operating the Hall process. However, for a successful suit they would have to prove to the court that the Cowles people were actually infringing the Hall patent. Securing the necessary evidence of this infringement was not going to be easy, since the Cowles operations were conducted with great secrecy.

Arthur Davis, the young superintendent of The Pittsburgh Reduction Company was sent to investigate and arrived in Lockport on February 21. The Cowles works, as he had been told, were located on an island. On one side flowed the race supplying water for the wheel turning the works' dynamo. On the other side was a spillway through which surplus water flowed, rejoining the main race again below the island. On the further side of the race rose a precipitous bluff which made access from that side extremely difficult. On the other side of the island was a bridge across the spillway, which was supposed to be the only way of getting on the island. This bridge was closed by a locked gate and guarded by a watchman.

After surveying the scene, Davis decided on a plan of action. Waiting until it was dark enough to conceal his movements, he clambered down the steep bluff to the level of the bulkhead holding back the mill pond. Reaching the bulkhead, fortunately without falling into the swiftly flowing waters of the mill race, he found a joist. Davis crawled across this timber and dropped safely to the ground on the island.

The Cowles people thought they had carefully hidden their new operations. All the doors in the pot room carried spring locks and the glass in the windows had been painted on the inside. On this particular evening, however, fumes in the pot room had become so bad that the workmen left one window open for ventilation, and Davis quickly spied this open window. Providentially also, there was a pile of brick beneath the window. Climbing on top of this pile, Davis looked through the window and leisurely surveyed the scene. He saw a line of iron-shelled reduction pots with their carbon anodes and supporting copper rods hanging from an electric bus, just as in the works at Smallman Street.

The details of this adventurous inspection were very clear in Mr. Davis' mind when he testified to them just two months later. During cross-examination no one thought to ask Mr. Davis how he had escaped from the island. Perhaps he walked

157

Arthur Vining Davis, young superintendent of Smallman Street Works, about 1893

over the bridge across the spillway without detection when the night shift was changed the following morning.

Davis left Lockport the next day, but not until he had taken the precaution of hiring Frederick Rossiter, who had been working as a furnace man at the Cowles plant for the past twenty months. Rossiter had been running the Cowles' new reduction pots under the direction of John Hobbs, the foreman of the pot room which had been the object of Mr.

158

Davis' nocturnal inspection. During the patent suit, Rossiter was able to testify that the Cowles Company was using the same process as The Pittsburgh Reduction Company at Pittsburgh, where he had been working since leaving Lockport. As mementos of his work at Lockport, Rossiter took with him samples of the electrolyte and alumina which were being employed at the Cowles plant. After analysis they came in very handy as part of the testimony supporting the claim of infringement against the Cowles Company.

The Pittsburgh Reduction Company promptly filed their suit against the Cowles Electric Smelting and Aluminum Company. A preliminary injunction against the Cowles' use of the process was requested pending disposal of the case. The injunction was not granted although the claim was pressed vigorously.

The taking of testimony before a special examiner began in Pittsburgh on April 27th. Here, Moore, Rossiter, Davis and Clapp told their story and John W. Langley, a metallurgical chemist from Pittsburgh testified as an expert witness in support of the Hall patent, U. S. No. 400,766.

The taking of testimony was adjourned to Lockport where, on June 30, the defendants called Eugene Cowles to present their side of the case. Cowles, testifying for seven days, told a type of story familiar to patent attorneys: The Cowles Company, he alleged, was not using the Hall patent; not even The Pittsburgh Reduction Company was using Hall's process. Furthermore, he alleged that Hall didn't invent the process he patented nor the process he was using in Pittsburgh; this process, Cowles claimed, was invented by the Cowles brothers, and if they didn't invent it, then it was a Frenchman named Deville or a Russian named Bogusky, if indeed several other foreigners didn't invent it first! This thesis was expounded by Eugene

159

Cowles in specious detail and *in extenso*. Eugene Cowles was followed by an "expert witness" and by his brother Alfred, both of whom elaborated on the arguments of Eugene.

Finally Hall was able to write Julia on August 30:

> "I am done with Lockport for the present and will be home in a day or two, probably Tuesday or Wednesday, if not before. The Cowles Company have finished their Lockport witness and now have only one more. They may take his testimony in Cleveland and possibly Philadelphia. I took a treat from Eugene Cowles last evening to the extent of some lemonade, but am feeling in my usual health today."

And Julia noted on the back of the envelope: "He was lucky to be in usual health after that treat."

Eventually the taking of testimony was completed and the attorneys for the two companies argued the case before Judge Taft (later President Taft) and Judge Ricks. The record was a voluminous one, over 1,500 pages, and Judge Taft "read with care" every page. When Judge Taft handed down his decision on January 20, 1893, it was a sweeping victory for Hall. The validity of his patent was upheld and the Cowles Company was adjudged guilty of infringement. In a detailed opinion, Judge Taft pointed out how the testimony in the case completely failed to support the Cowles Company's arguments. Judge Taft in his opinion stated:

> "Hall's process is a new discovery. It is a decided step forward in the art of making aluminum. Since it has been put into practical use, the price of aluminum has been reduced from six or eight dollars a pound to sixty-five cents. This is a revolution in the art and has had the effect of extending the uses of aluminum in many directions not

160

possible when its price was high. . . . Hall was a pioneer, and is entitled to the advantages which that fact gives him in the patent law."

This was a decision that was never reversed, either in a court of law or in the realm of technology. Hall was jubilant over the victory. For days and weeks he had to sit and listen to the Cowles' witnesses disparage his invention, but at last came his vindication. In 1893 he was able to write his classmates at Oberlin:

"There is very little to tell about myself. The most important thing that has happened to me during the past year has been the winning of a lawsuit which some of you know about. Personally, I was treated very kindly by the court in the case. The judges, Taft and Ricks of the United States Circuit Court of Ohio, sustained a patent of mine which was at issue, and gave me the honor of making a fundamental and pioneer invention of great value."

Justice had triumphed, but only for the moment. Even before Judge Taft had upheld the Hall patent, another legal cloud was appearing on the horizon. On February 2, 1892, a United States patent had been issued to Charles S. Bradley of Yonkers, New York. The claims appeared to cover the simultaneous fusion and electrolysis of a compound by means of the electric current. In due time, the owners would claim that The Pittsburgh Reduction Company infringed this patent by letting the heat of the electrolyzing current keep the cryolite bath molten—an event which could scarcely be avoided in the commercial operation of the Hall process. Controversies over the ownership and validity of this patent were to rage, in and out of court, for over ten years.

~ *13* ~

. . . *the letters Charles
wrote Julia*

WHEN CHARLES, in his hour of elation, wrote his brother George on the 24th of February in 1886, he cited the *Encyclopedia Britannica* to explain the electrochemistry of the great discovery he had just made. The *Britannica* by then had become a member of the family and was kept in Charles's bedroom in Oberlin. Alone in a boardinghouse in Pittsburgh, he missed the familiar volumes, and after a couple of years had the family ship the books to him. Charles assured Julia they would be given the care which such companions deserved:

"The encyclopedias were not at all injured in coming. I have them on the marble mantel shelf over the fireplace. They are all standing up straight and close together and are just as well off as though in a bookcase except exposed to the air and dust, but the chambermaid says she will cover them up when she sweeps the room. Ask Father if he thinks a bookcase is necessary for them."

Arthur Davis on many occasions had observed Hall's preoccupation with these volumes:

> "He used to read the *Encyclopedia Britannica* night after night, year after year, literally; that was his Mark Twain, detective stories, and everything all put together. He used to get down the *Encyclopedia* and open it wherever it happened to open; then he would spend the evening reading, and he accumulated a big fund of information in that manner."

Charles was hungry for information on science and invention, but his interests also wandered into literary fields. In Pittsburgh, he could occasionally be seen haunting bookstores. One of his favorite shops met with a calamitous accident one day, and Charles's family, reading about it in the Oberlin newspaper, were concerned until he reassured them:

> "I was four miles away, in bed and asleep at the time . . . I saw the pile of bricks and mortar where that building fell the other day. There were fifteen people killed altogether. I had been in the bookstore that part of it fell onto, and was going there again at the first opportunity."

Hall was an omnivorous reader at times, but he was not essentially bookish. For him, books were only one road to knowledge. Even though he may never have heard Louis Agassiz' admonition "Study nature—not books," Hall was at heart an intelligent interpreter of natural phenomena and a tireless experimenter.

Though not particularly gregarious, the young inventor was interested in the many men around him who had made their mark. The industrial climate of Pittsburgh was one in which pioneers flourished. Although Hall was not conscious of the fact, he was playing a part in the technologic revolution which was to convert the United States from a primarily agricultural economy to an industrial one. Since boyhood, Hall had read about Westinghouse and his inventions. One evening while attending the Musical Festival he saw the great man and reported to Julia:

> "Friday evening I saw Mr. George Westinghouse across the house in one of the boxes. You know he is one of the great nabobs of Pittsburgh and has made twenty millions out of his inventions."

Other prominent Pittsburghers were interested in the young aluminum company in these early days. Andrew W. Mellon and his brother R. B. visited the Smallman Street works one afternoon. Hall sold A. W. Mellon his first sixty shares of Pittsburgh Reduction Company stock in 1890, and Mr. Mellon served as treasurer for a few weeks in 1892. Soon after William Thaw, Jr., became a director of the company in 1890, Charles wrote Julia: "He is a man who is worth several millions, but enjoys poor health . . . He is a very nice man and a man of very great ability and shrewdness in business affairs."

The Pittsburgh Reduction Company had an exhibit at the Pittsburgh Exposition in October, 1889, and showed the public the astonishing sight of a ton of aluminum ingots. Here, Hall met and talked with Brashear, the famous maker of optical instruments. He tried to interest Brashear in the use of aluminum but was told it could not be used in instruments until it was "a little cheaper, as $2.00 a pound." It wasn't many years before a Buffalo paper referred to Hall as "the inventor of aluminum," a phrasing which Charles found very intriguing.

Throughout life, music and invention were Hall's most absorbing interests. Even when living in cramped quarters, a rented piano was installed if at all possible. In '91 he wrote Julia:

"'The duck who runs the gospel mill next door,' as Shakespeare says, has taken quite a liking to my piano (I mean the minister). I have had quite a number of compliments on my piano playing, which is quite as audible in a number of rooms as in my own. . . . Mrs. Smith says she likes the sound of the piano, and so do other people who I was afraid might object—which is a consolation."

The sequel came next week, however, when he reported:

"I have been waited on and requested not to play my piano during church services next door. . . . I went to church next door this morning. I hope it will be counted to my credit for I didn't enjoy myself there. . . . The Sunday School holds forth about fifteen feet from my window and the windows are open. It sounds as though there were a good many people there who had the faculty of talking continuously without saying anything—you know how a large Sunday school sounds."

Charles seemed to have some candid impressions of Sunday school, for in another letter he remarked:

"I wonder how Louie likes Sunday school teaching. I believe it is good experience. It teaches one to talk uninterruptedly without saying anything in particular—isn't that so?"

When opportunity offered and cash-in-pocket permitted, Hall seldom passed up good music. Several times he had the pleasure of attending Rosenthal's concerts. Moritz Rosenthal was a young pianist of Austrian birth who had studied with

Joseffy and Liszt. Only a year older than Hall, Rosenthal was acquiring an international reputation for his mastery of the piano. On one occasion Hall purchased a ticket to Rosenthal's concert even though he was "pretty near broke" and had less than ten dollars left when his board was paid. Hall said the music was "very good. I wonder if he will be in Oberlin. I sent my own piano back to the store two months ago. There was no use in keeping it as I had no time to use it."

On another occasion a fellow-boarder, who was a member of the Mozart Club, gave Hall two tickets to their concert. Hall found it "annoying" that he only had use for one. Probably he had forgotten about "the minister's daughter across the street" whose acquaintance he had made recently!

The Music Festival was a May event in Pittsburgh that also strained the Hall pocketbook. He wrote Julia: "I have already spent five dollars on tickets and may spend more." Intrigued by the opera he reported: "I am going to the Opera house tomorrow night to hear Faust. That will make three times I have been to a theatre this year."

In the spring of '89, Hall was laboring on the first technical paper he had ever attempted. At the moment, he had "not made much headway" but eventually he had the able assistance of Captain Hunt as a coauthor. This paper, under the title "The Properties of Aluminum with Some Information Relating to the Metal," by Alfred E. Hunt, John W. Langley, and Charles M. Hall, was presented at a meeting of the American Institute of Mining Engineers in Washington, D. C. on February 21, 1890. The third session of the Institute's meeting was entirely devoted to aluminum, and the leading paper was that of Hunt, Langley and Hall. The thirty-five pages of this paper were filled with important new information on the composition, mechanical properties and other useful characteristics of

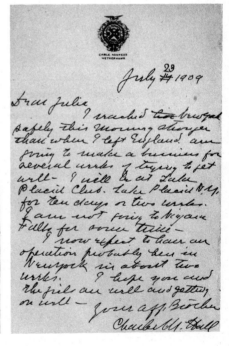

Pages from three Hall letters, showing handwriting in 1882, 1887, 1909

aluminum. At this meeting Hall received the honor of being elected a member of the American Institute of Mining Engineers.

Hall wrote few articles for the technical press. He was goaded into writing the next one by reading an article dealing with aluminum in one of the journals of the electrical industry. In his opinion, the publication of the article was inspired by the U. S. Aluminum Metal Company, a competitor which was trying at the time to promote the Héroult aluminum alloy process in the United States. Julia learned about her brother's latest literary effort in this manner:

"Last Sunday I spent most all the afternoon and evening before and after church—for I did go to church—in writing a most violent and intemperate article for the electrical papers. Literary work, among people who work every day, is considered a most appropriate form of employment for Sunday among people who belong to one church and attend another in the same city with great regularity. I remember that at college literary work, being like the work of every other day, was considered desecration of the Sabbath, but in the business life of a city it is a suitable occupation. Well, I spent last Sunday that way, anyhow. You remember the article in the *Western Electrician* that you sent me, which you considered to be inspired by the Cowles Co. Well, at the meeting where that paper was read some people discussed aluminum itself and said it was only a third as strong as iron, was easily corroded, was in fact no better than tin or zinc and had the added disadvantage of lightness, and that the only reason it acquired any reputation was because it had had attributed to it the qualities of its alloys. The whole discussion was false and ridiculously untrue. It was published first in the *Electrical World*. So I wrote an answer and waded into the man and his ideas as well as I was able, and Monday, Miss Kuester, Captain Hunt's typewriter girl, copied it in typewriter and sent it to four of the electrical papers and also to the American Manufacturer. We haven't heard from it since. I don't know whether anyone will publish it or not, but if they do I will send you a copy."

Hall's eager defense of the metal he loved received prompt attention from the editors, for in a couple of weeks he wrote Julia "that it was published by all the electrical papers to which it was sent." His contribution as it appeared in *Western Electrician* for May 30, 1891, hardly lived up to the flaming advance notices he had given Julia. His impatience with Prof. Crocker duly vented, he had written a well-considered argument for aluminum:

"It has been stated by Professor F. B. Crocker in an article on the 'Properties of Aluminum,' that ninety-nine persons out of every hundred have entirely wrong ideas regarding that metal. This statement I am more inclined to believe since reading Professor Crocker's own article. His statements regarding the properties of aluminum are so wide of the mark and so misleading that they ought to be corrected."

Hall then proceeded to correct the professor's errors in some two thousand words with just an occasional touch of mildly modulated sarcasm. Hall concluded with a prophetic statement:

"The world has been centuries in learning to use other metals; in learning to roll, draw, temper and polish them. Aluminum is new, but we are learning how to deal with it, how to secure the qualities of strength, hardness, ductility, lustre, etc., when required, much more rapidly than has occurred in the history of the other metals."

Even in a changing world, it was going to take decades for Hall's company to teach thousands of new users how to fabricate aluminum and to appreciate the advantages of strength and lightness in anything that has to move on land, sea or in the air.

Hall's published contributions to the literature of aluminum were strictly limited in number. This couldn't have been from lack of ability in writing, for he wrote innumerable letters to his business associates. These business letters had little of personal interest in them, but they bring out the man's competent grasp of the innumerable technical and commercial details of the company's growing business. They also illustrate the dogged persistence with which he worked for a solution of the company's technical problems.

Charles's pen was on parade when writing his contributions to the Oberlin Class of '85 Annual. These letters—twenty-one in twenty-nine years—gave to his classmates, interesting accounts of his activities, travels and an occasional note on his health. They portray vividly the zest with which a young man from the Ohio countryside viewed historic spots in America, England and Europe. Through the passing years, they trace high points in the growth of his professional career and his physical decline, philosophically related.

It would be helpful in understanding Charles, if the letters that Julia wrote him were available, for they would certainly tell something of their mutual problems. Little is known about Julia's letters, but living in a boardinghouse with curious chambermaids presented security problems that Charles solved either by fragmentation, combustion or by use of lock and key.

He wrote Julia:

"If Mrs. R. likes to read my letters, I hope she has a nice time of it. I leave enough of them in her way except yours, that you are particular about. Since I have known her. . . . I think Mark Twain had a good reason for writing as he did about chambermaids."

And on another occasion:

"I had the usual number of letters from you last week, and have not much to write today. I have forgotten probably the questions you asked, as I followed your suggestion and burned your letter as soon as I knew what was in it."

Julia had a low opinion of Charles as a public speaker, for on the back of one of his letters, she wrote:

"His college orations made him groan and sometimes quite profane. He used to rehearse them to me, not that he forgot, but speaking was not his strong point, and it bored him."

Even if not an accomplished public speaker, Hall exhibited an agile mind and literate tongue on the several occasions when he testified in defense of his patent. Though he sometimes gave vent to well-modulated profanity, in his letters to Julia, at least, he was careful to spell certain words such as d——l and h——l with significant spacing to indicate the missing letters. This manner of spelling was only a concession to convention for he wrote the shocking words with silent satisfaction.

Hall was convinced that alcohol and tobacco were the inventions of the devil. He had, however, no inhibitions about playing whist with friends when opportunity offered. On occasion, he could even twit his friends about their addiction to tobacco:

> "I have evolved a theory for the amusement of my tobacco-using friends that one great reason why all modern artistic work is so inferior to that of former centuries is that the various narcotics introduced within the last two or three centuries (tobacco among the Westerns and opium among the Orientals) has produced a deterioration of human nerve tissue."

The letters which Charles wrote Julia, and which she preserved, are a slender thread to guide the biographer to the inner man. The protective secrecy with which Charles habitually surrounded his embryo inventions and business affairs also became a cloak for his hopes and disappointments, frustrations and fears. To many of his coworkers, Charles was a peculiar man. Individualistic in thought and action, he seldom considered it necessary to explain himself. He was so essentially logical, however, that no one who knew him could characterize his behavior as haphazard. His every action must have been conditioned by experience, even though long forgotten. Charles was not bothered by modern psychological theory; he took himself for granted and never pretended to be anyone else.

14

. . . Mr. Hall is making gold in there

THE YEAR 1895 was an important one in Hall's calendar.
Thirteen years before, Charles had hopefully written Julia:
"Yes, I really think I shall be a rich inventor some day." That
day had arrived. In March of 1895, The Pittsburgh Reduction
Company declared its first dividend, a quarterly payment of
two dollars per share. Three more two-dollar dividends were
to follow before the year was finished.

Judge Taft had placed his seal of approval on Hall's invention when he ruled it a pioneering discovery. Now Hall was
to have ready cash as well as stock in his safe deposit box. He
had become a rich inventor. The company's policy of frugal
living was bearing fruit, and the stockholders were being
rewarded for their patience.

When the company issued the new stock in October,
1889, Charles had generously remembered his family. He presented his father and his sisters, Julia, Edith and Louie with a

block of four hundred shares. This stock with stock dividend accretions remained closely held by one or the other of the original recipients until long after Charles's death.

It is not surprising that the largest certificate was registered in Julia's name for she was his closest personal friend and confidante. Even with Julia, his recorded confidences were regulated as to subject and circumstance, for Charles seldom put on paper anything about his secret projects which might, even by accident, suffer premature disclosure. To his father, Charles showed a respectful affection. The young man, walking arm in arm with the white-haired Reverend Hall, was a familiar scene to Oberliners. Even before their mother's untimely passing, Charles acquired a protective attitude toward his younger sisters, Edith and Louie. This group constituted the home circle, since sister Emily had married a missionary and gone to China—a situation which lacked Charles's approval—and brother George was preaching in Dover, New Hampshire.

Since the futile attempt to promote his invention in Boston in 1886, Charles had little news or contact with his brother George. It was then that skeptical George advised him to forget his passionate pursuit of invention, find a job and start supporting himself. In April of '89, when his aluminum process was finally in commercial operation, Charles inquired of Julia:

"Do you ever hear anything from the old boy? I have a curiosity to know what he will say when he finds that his prophecies have failed, but I am not anxious to have anyone write and tell him about it."

Two years later, Charles wrote again: "Do you ever hear from the old boy? An article in the last *News* referred to him as giving an address at the meeting of the New England Oberlin Alumni Association." After another two years had passed, Charles gave George a substantial present—one hundred shares of the stock of The Pittsburgh Reduction Company. In 1894, he added another hundred shares. Time was beginning to show its healing effects, but not for long. In 1896, Charles was provoked again at his brother for disposing of the stock he had given him. Such lack of faith in the company was offensive to its founder.

Just a year after pouring the first ingot of aluminum at Smallman Street, Hall was pondering the next step for the growing company:

"I think for the next enlargement if made soon we better use steam power. Then the works will be all together; the running expenses may be a little more but the investment required will be less. I think we ought to find out more about water power, however. Hunt told me there was 10,000 h.p. at Rochester, N. Y. that we could get. We ought to find out what it would cost."

The next enlargement of the works was at New Kensington, and electricity from a steam-powered generator was employed for several years to operate the reduction pots. In this manner, the production of aluminum was increased to 1,000 pounds per day in 1893. Hall also moved to New Kensington to be near the scene of operations, where he was kept busy with new production problems. In a personal way, the move only meant a change in boardinghouses, but at least it was a change.

The company's quest for cheap electric power was realized in 1893 when its first contract was signed with Niagara Falls Power Company, calling for 1,500 horsepower with an option on an additional 1,000 horsepower. The new reduction works posed new design problems and the plant was not finished and put into operation until August, 1895. Then, for the first time, the company was really in position to lower the cost of aluminum and reach out for bigger markets.

The year 1895 was also an important one for Hall in a personal way. When the company moved its reduction works from New Kensington, Hall moved to Niagara Falls, which henceforth was to be his home city. For some years he lived in rented rooms, but eventually his dream of a residence where he could receive and entertain his friends was realized.

From the time of his arrival at Niagara, Hall was kept busy at the new aluminum works. The possibilities in the use of 1,500 horsepower for making aluminum were completely absorbing, but only for a few months. Research, with Charles, was a fundamental hunger. Eating was an essential fueling operation necessary for the human machine, but the craving for research supplied a drive which seldom faltered even when the machine showed the effects of wear and tear.

It was only natural, therefore, that the old battery scheme should begin to absorb his attention. Ideas long fallow, now bloomed with the spring and Hall was at it again. With money of his own to hire a chemist just for this work, he was well fortified to attack again this hardy technical perennial.

The porous metallic electrodes that Hall had made for his fuel cell in 1891 didn't function as anticipated. The failure Hall attributed to their lack of catalytic activity. He was sure that platinum or rhodium with their well-known catalytic properties would work, but these metals were too expensive and he started a search for some cheaper but effective substitute.

Again he had recourse to electricity and started working with powerful spark discharges between electrodes immersed in aqueous solutions. Hall soon produced a very small amount of a material which he could not identify, but its chemical behavior led him to believe that it might be an unknown compound of iron. As his excitement grew, he even speculated on the possibility that he had transmuted iron into a metal of the platinum group such as rhodium. Finally he could contain himself no longer and wrote, longhand, a series of ten very confidential letters to Captain Hunt. These were all marked "Personal" and kept in a secret file. The story can be told in condensed form by a series of excerpts selected from these long-concealed letters.

"My Dear Captain,   May 1896

Personal

"Our relations in the aluminum business have been so satisfactory, to me at least, that I should naturally turn to you first in anything new. . . . My main object in starting these experiments was to perfect a scheme for the production of electricity directly from fuel. I have had such a scheme since 1882 which I have spent more than three solid years of work on and a number of thousands of dollars . . . At present it depends on . . . the use of metals of the platinum series of which palladium and rhodium are the most efficient for causing the oxidation of carbon and hydrogen compounds at ordinary temperatures.

"I have formed somewhat of a theory as to the way in which the spark under water operates in producing the results obtained . . . The water is incompressible and possesses considerable inertia . . . acts as a kind of 'tamping' so that there is present both the decomposing effect of the spark and also what is equivalent to enormous pressure . . . in the nature of a tremendous blow . . . forcing the atoms of water into closer juxtaposition . . . I have succeeded recently in making some metals, from iron, which are evidently very close to the platinum metals if not actually the same . . . The process seems to me now essentially one of densification or condensation . . . The reaction I imagine is something like this:

"Iron (56) plus 4 carbon (48) = rhodium (104). At any rate I get something having very near the properties of rhodium by treating iron with carbon . . . either a carbide of iron. . . .

"(June) I saw Dr. Chandler this morning. He said that what I had to tell him was extremely interesting. He should advise going right ahead, working night and day. No one could tell, he said, what might be done. He also advised getting the assistance of a chemist of ability . . . Since Mr. Jeans came he has been making a good many analyses of the material used and products made . . . The results show that what I had supposed to be tin and copper and possibly some of the platinum metals, turns out to be only tin and copper . . . This seems like reducing the accomplishments so far to a rather 'small bulk' to use the chemist's expression . . . There was one time when I thought myself that there was nothing to the whole business except impure material. I don't think so now that we have also taken unusual care with crucible and everything like that . . .

"(November) I believe that I have gotten hold of a new principle in metallurgy of the greatest importance.

"(February, 1897) My recent experiments consist in subjecting molten iron and alloys in a kind of trough of magnesia to the action of low voltage current of large quantity . . . 2,000 to 4,500 amperes . . . iron treated in the above way for one to two hours appears to contain a considerable amount (estimated from 5% to 10%) of an apparently new metal."

181

During a visit to the Niagara aluminum works during this period, Captain Hunt's son Roy stopped before a closed laboratory door marked NO ADMITTANCE. "What," he asked his guide, "is causing that tremendous crackling noise? Sounds like a powerful electric spark." "We don't know," was the whispered reply, "but there is a rumor that Mr. Hall is making gold in there."

For centuries the transmutation of metals had been placed in the category of black magic. Even though orthodox chemists considered the atom indivisible and unchangeable, Hall pursued with frenzied activity, experiments which seemed to indicate otherwise. Hall was not one to be deterred, as he wrote Captain Hunt, "by investigations in which there is commonly supposed to be 'no thoroughfare.' " Had not the eminent Dr. Chandler of Columbia University encouraged his latest investigation?

Röntgen in 1895 had just discovered astonishing X-rays which could penetrate solid matter. A year later Becquerel found a mysterious radiation given off by a uranium-containing mineral. Soon Madame Curie and her husband were on the trail of the radioactive agents in pitchblende and announced the discovery of radium in 1898. Although the significance of these discoveries was not yet apparent, both chemists and physicists had found keys which were eventually to help unlock the secrets of the atom.

Hall's fantastic idea that he might be able to transmute metals doesn't seem so ridiculous now that it has been accomplished, though by other means than those Hall had at his disposal. Hall's every "successful" experiment seemed to evaporate before the test of diligent analysis, but these failures did not completely discourage him.

Ordinarily quite confiding in his letters to Julia, Charles did

182

not give her any details of this project until April of 1904.

"In order to gratify your enormous curiosity as to what my enormous scheme is, I will tell you that it is an attempt to make certain rare metals from common metals and other common chemical elements. I want these rare metals for use in my battery scheme . . . I am still working on my enormous scheme. The scheme is looking up some and have reason to believe I am going to get there . . . I am very busy at this now."

Hall's experiments, though unique, led up a blind alley to final disappointment; but while the excitement lasted, he had dreams of another revolutionary discovery which would startle scientists the world around.

This is the last record of Hall's battery scheme which has been discovered. No doubt, however, Hall kept thinking about it from time to time as long as he lived. The dream of developing a practical fuel cell did not die with Hall's passing. The issue of *Iron Age* for July 10, 1952 carried an article entitled "Aluminum: A new Energy Source: from which the following sentences are selected:

"The aluminum industry is tied to cheap power. And Pittsburgh Consolidation Coal Co. has come up with something that may prove the answer for cheap electricity from coal . . . Normal method of generating electricity with coal is to turn a generator with a steam turbine. The new method, still in experimental stages, eliminates the turbine and substitutes a battery-like 'fuel cell' for the generator . . . expected to result in an amazing efficiency of near 80 per cent, according to Pittsburgh Consol. Conventional steam turbine generating plants transform only about 35 per cent of the fuel energy into electricity . . . The conservative scientists are quick to stress that the process is still at the experimental point and there are many unknowns yet to be solved."

Hall's lifetime struggle with the fuel cell did not reach its objective, but the by-products of this research led him along other avenues of investigation which were even more fascinating.

～の 15 ～の

. . . *Captain Hunt*
answers the call to arms

EXCITING as were his "enormous" schemes for making platinum and rhodium from iron, Hall had plenty of everyday troubles in the making and marketing of aluminum at the new Niagara works. Some of these were minor incidents and had their humorous aspects. A shipment of scrap aluminum from the Illinois Pure Aluminum Company arrived 85½ pounds short and was reported to the Pittsburgh office:

> "Fifty pounds of this shortage came from part of an old iron cooking stove, tin oil cans, screws, nails, two old shirts, cloth off buffing wheels, etc. From the looks of some of this scrap it appears that they scraped up the floor and put everything in they happened to scrape up."

On another occasion Mr. Hall, tho vice-president of The Pittsburgh Reduction Company, had to investigate the matter of a kitchen sink, made from the company's aluminum. He made a trip to Buffalo and examined the complaining sink, after which he wrote a long letter to the manufacturer:

"I called on Mr. H. Hamlin Monday and saw the aluminum sink. It is what I would call a perfect casting and a very creditable piece of work entirely satisfactory except in regard to the color and polish. It does not have the bright polish and color which aluminum maintains under favorable conditions but is dark and has somewhat an appearance of oxidized silver. It seems to have been impossible to get the bright color similar to nickel plate and silver, which Mr. Hamlin said he expected and claims that he specified in ordering the sink.

"Captain Hunt has an aluminum bathtub in his house at Pittsburgh, which is rubbed dry and polished every few days and kept dry when not in use. This is as bright as silver. He also has an aluminum sink and slab which I have seen only once, but my impression is that it is not bright and silvery but looks more nearly as Mr. Hamlin's does, although it is entirely satisfactory to Captain Hunt.

"Mr. Hamlin was in a very unpleasant frame of mind in regard to the sink. He seemed to regard me as having come there to help collect the bill, which I knew nothing about and had nothing to do with. The first thing which he said on entering the room was that he would not pay the bill for the sink, and that was the last thing which he said on my leaving, and it was the burden of his talk all the time I was there. I offered to get some polish from Pittsburgh for him to try and to find out how Captain Hunt kept his aluminum bathtub as bright, but Mr. Hamlin claimed that he had tried everything and I think from the appearance of the

187

sink that a good deal of labor had been put on it to try to polish it, and would do nothing further. He seemed to resent any suggestion which I had for making the sink satisfactory. He has made up his mind, evidently, that it was unsatisfactory and that he would try nothing more to make it right. I regret that the interview had no better result in this respect.

Yours very truly
The Pittsburgh Reduction Co.
Charles M. Hall, vice-pres."

Of more serious import were electric power stoppages. In those days, dynamo-electric equipment was not the well-trained servant it has since become. Handling the huge amount of Niagara power at their command, brought crises which Hall and his associates had little experience in meeting. After one wild day at Niagara, Hall described the situation to Captain Hunt in these words:

"On reaching the works this morning, I found the state of affairs very much as we were led to believe from Mr. Dickey's telephone message yesterday. One of the rotary transformers had burst at the commutator end, throwing copper and iron in all directions with corresponding damage. Some of the pieces had struck one of the other rotarys, knocking down the switchboard and connections so that it will take several days to repair it. A hole about 6 x 10 feet was knocked through our brick wall on the river side of the transformer room. One piece weighing 800 pounds fell into our pot room and onto the line. The velocity must have been enormous. No one was hurt by the accident."

Later in the year, Hall reported that the situation was improved but still needed watching:

"With machinery as expensive as this is, and the possibilities of expensive accidents and the certainty of deterioration if the best care is not afforded, I should be simply afraid to continue the present arrangement after the Westinghouse men are out of the place.

"You say that you think I ought to give the matter my regular and careful attention. This I certainly expect to do, but I cannot spend over two or three hours in the dynamo room each day and that is not enough. . . . Each set of dynamos should be shut down every few days and thoroughly cleaned up, the commutators polished, the brushes and brush holders repaired and the copper dust and carbon dust which accumulates in the winding, blown out with an air blast. If this is not done, the dynamos will heat and the insulation would deteriorate. As a result we would have several thousands of dollars in repair bills every year.

"Another thing which I would be afraid to leave to the men in the powerhouse is the operation of changing from one set of machinery to another. Even the Westinghouse men have not been able to do this successfully without trouble. On one occasion it took them an hour to get the four machines to run together—not through any fault of the dynamos but in the setting of the brush holders or something of the kind."

To keep the dynamos in good running order, Hall asked permission from Captain Hunt to put them in charge of an electrical engineer. Frederick A. Stoughton, a young man trained at Kimball Union and with practical experience at General Electric Company, was given the job of making the electric power behave. He soon mastered the machinery and saved Hall many a headache. Stoughton grew with the job

189

and made handling electric power for the aluminum company a lifetime career.

After production of aluminum with hydroelectric power had been inaugurated, the next point of attack on the cost problem was in the raw material field. Each pound of aluminum required two pounds of pure alumina and two-thirds of a pound of carbon electrode. The company had been buying alumina, some produced domestically and some imported. Not only was cost an important item, but difficulty was experienced in securing alumina of the proper quality.

Bauxite, which is the ore from which alumina is obtained, was discovered in Arkansas in 1887, almost at the same time that Hall discovered his process for making aluminum. Now the management trio of Hunt, Hall and Davis was looking forward to the time when the company might own a bauxite mine or two and produce refined alumina to their own specifications.

Patent situations were also a cause of concern to the management. Not only had the production of aluminum stopped at their plant at Patricroft in England, but the British Aluminum Company was trying to prevent the importation and sale of Hall's aluminum in England. The Bradley patent, which was alleged to cover the heating of the cryolite bath with the electrolyzing current, had finally found an owner. The inventor had made a deal with Grosvenor P. Lowrey to promote it but, as soon as the patent was granted, the Cowles Company laid claim under their interpretation of an agreement made seven years before with Bradley. The first court decided that the patent belonged to Bradley and Lowrey but the Court of Appeals reversed this decision and awarded it to the Cowles Company on February 15, 1897. Hall and his associates had been following the course of this patent through the courts

190

with considerable interest and were not taken by surprise when the Cowles Company threatened suit against The Pittsburgh Reduction Company.

The upturn in business which eventually followed the panic of 1893, gave sufficient encouragement to the company to pay their first quarterly dividend in 1895. The improvement did not continue, however, and after five quarterly payments, dividends were suspended. The campaign for the free coinage of silver was one business depressant among others, and prosperity did not return until 1898.

Despite the nation's turmoil, the aluminum business continued to grow slowly, and as it grew, the company required more and more of Captain Hunt's time as well as Hall's. Hunt still found time, however, to be a good citizen, and was active in such movements as the purification of Pittsburgh's water supply, and mitigating the smoke pall which was the unpopular insigne of the city's industrial eminence.

Hunt's devotion to his country found expression in years of service as captain of artillery in the National Guard. Hampton Battery B which he commanded, offered its services in the Spanish War within twenty-four hours after President McKinley's call for troops in 1898. Every man volunteered. The war was not a long one and, when it was over, Captain Hunt compared notes with an old friend, Captain Brown of the 1st U. S. Cavalry:

October 20, 1898

"My dear Captain,

"I think you know my Battery entered the Volunteer Service on April 27, 1898, five days after the declaration of War. Every member of my Battery volunteered for the service, and we were ordered to Chickamauga with the

United States Volunteer Artillery, under Brig. Gen. E. B. Williston. I served in Williston's Light Battery 1883-85 at Ft. Leavenworth. We were under drill and being licked into shape during the months of June and July. I unfortunately contracted malarial fever and was sick in my quarters most of the time at Chickamauga. About the 15th of July my Battery was ordered to Puerto Rico. I got up off of a sick-bed and gave up my sick-leave and went with the Battery to Puerto Rico, and we had quite an experience, there being four Batteries, under Maj. Rodney, of artillery, of which I was senior captain—in fact, I was senior captain of Volunteer Artillery of the service in the Spanish War.

"The experience we had in Puerto Rico I shall write you further of when I have more time and you have swapped some of your experience at Santiago.

"My Battery was the one at the advance outpost of Gen. Brooke's column, and was just ready to pitch into what would have been one of the most severe engagements of the War when the peace protocol was presented to Gen. Brooke and prevented the action then in hand. Gen. Brooke had the only battle line formation that had been made of a whole division of troops on the Island of Puerto Rico. The first corps was all practically lined up for what would have been a pretty lively fight, for the Spaniards were pretty well fortified.

"After the cessation of hostilities, as I was still suffering from malaria and chills, I started for the United States, although I did not arrive more than ten days ahead of my Battery, as I came up on the *Gloucester* part way, and thereafter on the U. S. cruiser *Columbia,* which had orders to break the blockade, going around Puerto Rico and Cuba. In this way I was able to stop at Guantanamo, Santiago, and other places; saw Cevera's wrecked ships; and we were the first vessel into Havana and notified Gen. Blanco there of the blockade being broken and the port of Havana open. Thereafter, we went to Key West, where there was a pretty heavy dose of yellow fever at the time; and from there up to League Island Navy Yard, Philadelphia, from which I came home.

"I have been at home since and my Battery is now on furlough and will be mustered out by the first of December.

"This much for my whereabouts! Now swap and tell me of yours.

Yours fraternally,

Alfred E. Hunt

Capt. of Artillery,

Commanding Battery 'B',

Pa. Volunteers, U.S.A."

After the festivities for returning troops were over and he had taken a little rest, Captain Hunt reviewed the business situation and the problems he had left behind so hastily when he left for the army. Encouraged by signs of reviving commercial activity, the company sold six thousand shares of preferred stock in January of '99 and dividends were resumed in February. He started planning enlargement of the aluminum works at New Kensington and Niagara and the acquisition of bauxite mines, and took Hall on a trip to Arkansas for an investigation in person of bauxite mining prospects.

The captain did not realize until it was too late, how heavily he was drawing upon his reserve strength, already seriously impaired by exposure and illness at Chickamauga and Puerto Rico. He knew that a vacation was in order, however, and started for Atlantic City with his wife and mother. The party

Captain Alfred E. Hunt, Commanding Battery "B", Pennsylvania Volunteers, U.S.A.

stopped for a few days at the Hotel Lafayette in Philadelphia where the captain became seriously ill. His condition, complicated by a cardiac disorder and a minor operation, rapidly worsened, and he died unexpectedly on April 26, 1899.

194

In his annual letter to his Oberlin classmates, Hall told of the captain's passing:

"I have lately met with a severe loss in the sudden and untimely death of Captain Alfred E. Hunt, the president of our company, and my friend and co-worker for the last eleven years. His death was in a measure a sacrifice for his country. He enlisted for the Spanish War last year and was one of the few good officers of the volunteers. He contracted malaria at one of the worst of the army camps, and afterwards went to Puerto Rico, but never fully recovered from the disease and from the hardships of the experience. His death at the last however was sudden and unexpected. Captain Hunt's passing away has left a large place vacant. It would seem impossible to find a more pleasant friend, or a more energetic and able co-worker.

"In March I enjoyed a new experience in spending a few days in Arkansas partly in the woods near Hot Springs. Captain Hunt was with me on this trip. One day we were talking about death and the belief in a hereafter, little thinking of what should happen to one of us in so short a time."

In the years that followed, Hall came face to face with death on more than one occasion. For him, the problem of the hereafter had urgency only because there were so many projects he must finish while life lasted.

195

16

. . . interested in several
new things

OF PATENT TROUBLES there seemed no end. The Bradley patent, when issued in 1892, was a matter of general interest to Hall and his associates. They had no idea, however, that it would eventually become a matter of great concern and even a threat against survival of The Pittsburgh Reduction Company. The Bradley patent was based upon an application filed in 1883 and claimed a monopoly on *any* electrolytic process for making aluminum in which the electric current employed for electrolysis was also used to heat the bath and keep it molten. As soon as the patent was issued, the Cowles Company claimed ownership on the basis of an old agreement made with Charles S. Bradley some seven years prior. The controversy was taken to the courts and, after a lengthy contest, the Cowles Company was declared the owner.

When Hall first started his process in the Smallman Street plant, he made sure he would have enough heat by installing a gas flame burning against the bottom of the steel shell. He had anticipated, however, that the large electric current he was going to use in this first commercial plant would generate sufficient heat to keep the cryolite bath molten, and in a few weeks he found that he could turn out the gas and do without external heating. Cowles claimed that as soon as Hall turned out the gas, he began to infringe the Bradley patent.

On March 31, 1897, within a few weeks after gaining title to the Bradley patent, the Cowles Company started suit against The Pittsburgh Reduction Company. The suit was a tedious affair. Searching through dusty files of patents, reading about Sir Humphry Davy's pioneering experiments with electrolysis, paging through scores of technical books and journals for suggestion or practice which might prove Bradley's claims to be old stuff, kept Hall busy for days and weeks at a time. Then came the game of guessing the moves of the opposition and marshaling the evidence to defeat the hated rival. Master-minding the expert witnesses became a steady job for Hall, and volumes of testimony were accumulated. After another four years, on October 22, 1901, Judge Hazel in the District Court handed down a welcome decision, declaring that The Pittsburgh Reduction Company *did not* infringe the Bradley patent even if it were valid. The Cowles Company appealed this decision, and after another two years, the Circuit Court said that The Pittsburgh Reduction Company *did* infringe. This was a terrific shock to the company, for Hall and his people were convinced from the way the testimony was going, that the case would be decided in their favor. It seemed ironical to Hall that he could be prevented from electrolyzing a solution of alumina in cryolite just because the current heated the bath, an electrical phenomenon which was not new and a result which could not be avoided when the process was operated on a commercial scale.

Judge Coxe closed his decision with the statement:

"Even were it possible to do so it is surely unnecessary to follow all of the excursions of the experts into the occult realms of electrochemical science. Some of these trails seem to vanish into thin air, others are lost in a desert of technicalities, and of others still it is true that he who attempts to travel them is quite likely to find himself wandering aimlessly 'through caverns measureless to man.' "

To Hall, who understood the basic facts in this controversy, there was no doubt that the judge himself had wandered aimlessly in a desert of technicalities without reaching the merits of the case.

The decision left the Cowles Company and The Pittsburgh Reduction Company in a dilemma. Admittedly, the Bradley process of itself was impractical for the production of aluminum, and the Cowles Company could not use the Hall process with alumina dissolved in cryolite. On the other hand, Hall couldn't keep the electric current from heating his electrolytic bath. A compromise was soon reached. For a matter of a quarter of a million dollars and certain annual royalties, The Pittsburgh Reduction Company received a license under the Bradley patent until it expired in 1909. This turned out to be a partial blessing. Since the Hall patent was to expire in 1906, the license under the Bradley patent insured them exclusive use of the Hall process for an additional three years. The settlement, however, pinched the corporation pocketbook, for the company was engaged in new plant construction calling for an expenditure of a million dollars.

Six years of living in rented rooms and boardinghouses in Niagara Falls would have been even more monotonous if not for the frequent business trips that Hall made. During the litigation over the Bradley patent there were numerous conferences with the company's attorneys in New York, Cleveland, Philadelphia, Washington and Pittsburgh. Other trips took Hall to new and distant places. The visit with Captain Hunt to the bauxite mines in Arkansas brought the added pleasure of the captain's congenial company. Long discussions on technical, historical and even philosophical topics made this a memorable journey for Charles. In search of electric power for aluminum, Hall went to Canada soon after the trip to Arkansas. As anticipated, the rushing waters of the St. Maurice River at Shawinigan Falls seemed made to order for an aluminum works, and it was not long before a plant was being built to use hydroelectric power already available at the Falls. Forest and stream had always fascinated Charles, and traveling through the wilds of Quebec with its endless stands of aromatic spruce was another new experience. In Massena, New York, close by the St. Lawrence River, another suitable location was found. By 1903, the prospects for aluminum were so bright that a third aluminum works was built at that location.

In spite of his growing wealth from dividends, Charles contented himself with a couple of rooms for too many years. The rigors of winter in Niagara Falls brought unnecessary hardships and tested his stamina. A letter to Julia in November 1900 gave a graphic picture of living conditions in his small apartment:

"I have gotten a stove in what Mrs. Jones calls my spare room today—I will have a good coal fire there and will sleep in a cold room. Mrs. Jones did get a gas stove for

201

my sleeping room, but the gas is not steady and the stove is no good. I think I shall get along all right. It is impossible to cut a door between the two rooms. It is not easy to get comfortable rooms at Niagara Falls. Mrs. Collins has been looking for two rooms for herself and daughter but unsuccessfully. I am very much better off than I might be.

"My cold is about well and I am much better generally than at any time since June. The hot weather always pulls me down, and just as soon as it is cold I pick up and gain weight and feel better in every way.

"I hope I can come to Cleveland for Thanksgiving and will if I am here unless something unusual prevents. I may be in N. Y. or Pittsburgh, however."

Even in rented rooms, Charles usually managed to squeeze in a piano, sometimes a grand piano. Thus equipped, the evenings were not so lonely, and on occasion he entertained friends in his makeshift apartment. At one period he had a private chemist, whom he paid out of his own pocket, working on his extracurricular inventions. This man, John Thomson, was a young graduate from Lehigh University. Thomson's labors did not end at the laboratory, for on many an evening he would be invited to Hall's apartment for a long program of classical music. Properly appareled for the occasion, he was Hall's entire audience for several hours while his employer played selections from Beethoven to Mozart. It would be near midnight before Hall would tire and send Thomson home for a few hours' sleep before reporting to the laboratory at eight next morning. Thomson believed that "Hoffman never got more out of a piano than Mr. Hall."

Learning how to spend money was a part of the art of living which Charles was slow to acquire. He was generous to his

Hall reading chemical journal, at Oberlin, 1906

family and civic minded in his contributions, but showed less
wisdom when it came to spending money for his own comfort
and welfare. By 1902, however, Charles decided he could
afford a home of his own and leased a spacious house at 136
Buffalo Avenue facing the rapids in Niagara River. Now he
could entertain at home—friends from Oberlin, business associates and other acquaintances who might be visiting Niagara
Falls. He could also experience the trials of a housekeeper.
Some of these are related in a letter he wrote Julia on the
Sunday after Christmas. After thanking her for towels and a
calendar which came in a Christmas package from home, he
gave the news:

203

"I reached home as I expected Friday morning. I was glad I came Thursday evening and it was lucky I did. The young man who stayed in the house let the fire go out and went off without kindling it, and the maid didn't get back till 3 o'clock or the housekeeper till 8 in the evening and by afternoon I think my fern and palms, of which I have four, would have been frozen. I think the said young man is a great booby."

In addition to the trials of housekeeping, Charles also had the problems of furnishing a house and one of these problems soon became a hobby—he started buying Oriental rugs. After some experiences which did not prove too expensive, he became a serious collector of Oriental rugs. The excitement of auctions was a diversion which he could enjoy, and the mistakes he made he could afford.

Hotel Schenley
Pittsburgh, Pa.
March 29, 1903

"There is a rug sale here at the hotel and I bought another rug, a small one of medium grade, but a very pretty one—and may get one or two more, but nothing expensive. There are absolutely no fine rugs here of the class to which my animal rug belongs, and last year there were a quantity. They are becoming rare. The people holding the sale are the largest importing firm in the country. They had one or two last year that I now wish I had bought."

On a later occasion, Charles was not so discriminating in his purchases:

"There has been an auction at Niagara Falls. Mrs. Elizabeth French, an English woman, formerly of Florence, Italy, who with Mr. F. are a queer combination, sold all their household goods. Like a chump I attended—it was quite a social event. I bid on two things and got one thing that I don't want, for probably three times what I could buy it for at a store. I bought a Japanese chocolate set. On getting it home, it looks cheap but don't look so bad a little way off. It is all gilt and colored painting. You can have it if you want it. Two of the cups are slightly cracked and one saucer, which I did I think. Mrs. French had a few nice things but I think the whole outfit sold for more than the things could have been bought for at reliable places. She had a few rare vases, a French clock, Japanese screens, etc. Her rugs were poor.

"If you want the chocolate set I will send it to you and will send at the same time if you want, one or two $8 and $9 rugs that also like a chump I bought in N. Y. the last time I was there. They are Bokhara rugs. They look pretty well at night but by daytime alongside good rugs, don't look so well. They were saddle covers. I won't loan these. If you take them I never want to see them again.

Your aff. brother

Charles M. Hall"

Niagara Falls, at the turn of the century, was the center of the rapidly growing electrochemical industry in America. Attracted by abundant electric power, the production of aluminum was followed by carborundum, artificial graphite, calcium carbide, fused alumina, caustic soda, sodium and other products of the electric furnace and the electrolytic cell. Those were boom days for electrochemistry in America and the American Electrochemical Society was formed in April 1902 to promote the interests of the electrochemist and publish a journal on electrochemistry. The organization meeting was held in Philadelphia but the society also had a strong group of members at the Falls. Charles Martin Hall was a charter member of the society, and was made a vice-president. Hall was already well known among scientists and inventors and was now on his way to becoming a public figure. This prominence was a matter of considerable inward satisfaction to Charles in that day of the Self-Made-Man.

One notable occasion in which Hall participated was a luncheon engagement of international importance. In 1902, Kaiser Wilhelm II sent his brother, Prince Henry of Prussia, to New York to represent him at a christening—the christening of the royal yacht then under construction in the United States. Prince Henry's visit was the occasion of many formal functions, including a luncheon for America's captains of industry. There was no question but that Hall represented the aluminum industry, and he accepted his invitation to the luncheon. At the last minute, someone in the company's management began to doubt whether Hall knew just what a captain of industry should wear for a formal luncheon. Safford K. Colby, a long-time employee of the company, and a personal friend, was given the assignment of checking on his sartorial arrangements. At 9:00 a.m. on the day of the luncheon, Colby hurried over to Hall's room (this is Colby's version), and found that the young inventor had his own ideas on suitable dress. He was planning to wear an ordinary business suit with a decorative necktie and high-buttoned yellow shoes. Hall was rather stubborn about some of Colby's suggestions and in particular objected to patent leather shoes because they "drew" his feet. As always, however, Colby was persuasive and overruled all objections. He rushed Hall to a clothing store, got him fitted with striped trousers, cutaway coat, wing collar, formal necktie, patent leather shoes and a derby hat. When Colby had Hall thus appareled, he rushed him out, called a cab, and delivered him personally at the 44th Street entrance to Sherry's. Thus was Charles Martin Hall, a representative of free enterprise and the aluminum industry, presented to royalty, in the person of Prince Henry of Prussia. What left the most lasting impression on Charles, however, was the sitting down to lunch with such famous Americans as Alexander Graham Bell, Thomas A. Edison and J. Pierpont Morgan.

Hall found a little publicity to his liking and began to expand his outside interests in the community. His financial stature as the major stockholder in The Pittsburgh Reduction Company was recognized when he was made a director in the Power City Bank. In his next class letter he mentioned a number of his new activities, and extended a cordial invitation to his Oberlin friends to visit him in his Niagara Falls home:

"Niagara Falls, N. Y.
136 Buffalo Ave.
June 5, 1903

"Dear Classmates:

"There is nothing special to write this year except that I am keeping house. I started to do so over a year ago at the above address, and am well satisfied with the experiment. I have had the pleasure of seeing several of the class under my roof. Anderegg was here last summer and Noble. Metcalf has been here twice, and I regret having missed Nyce, who called once, I think, when I was out of town. I hope I shall see others of the class this summer, and the same ones again.

"I have become interested in several new things lately. I am a bank director, belong to a committee of the local hospital, also a citizens' committee for the organization of

207

a Niagara Falls Y.M.C.A. and the erection of a building, the secretary of the latter being an Oberlin man of '98.

"Trusting to hear from many of you in the Annual, I remain,

Cordially yours,

Charles M. Hall"

Hall not only belonged to a committee of the Niagara Falls Memorial Hospital but that same year he was elected a trustee and its president. He served as president for eight years and only relinquished the latter office when forced to do so by failing strength. Hall was generous with both personal service and financial aid to the hospital, and was persuasive in bringing heads of other industries to the support of this fine institution.

In those days the bicycle was a popular vehicle for getting around both town and country, and it was Hall's custom to ride back and forth from house to work. Hall's bicycle was not only a means of transportation but on occasion afforded an introduction to other prominent electrochemists in the neighborhood. One fine Sunday, Charlie Hall went for a spin on his bicycle to Port Colborne, Ontario. Frank J. Tone, superintendent of the Carborundum Company and Max Mauran of the Castner Alkali works made it a party of three. As Mr. Tone has told the story:

Max got into conversation with Charlie, whom he had never met, and he asked Charlie where he worked.

"At The Pittsburgh Reduction Company," said Charlie.

"Oh yes," said Max, "they say that fellow Hall is a queer chap—like all those inventors, I suppose. My plant, the Castner Alkali works, is right next door to the aluminum works but I have never laid eyes on Hall. I suppose you know Hall. By the way, I did not get your name."

"My name is Hall," was the reply.

"Well, I'll be damned," said Max, "I thought you were one of those young chemists."

Charley Bradley, who started his career in aluminum at the Smallman Street works, continued as impresario of the pot rooms at the Niagara works. Working shoulder to shoulder with Charlie Hall on many an experimental job, Charley Bradley became a good friend and great admirer of the man. He remembers Hall as a terrific worker who gave little heed to the details of living when in hot pursuit of some technical discovery. There was one memorable experiment on which the two Charlies worked day and night for quite a period but Hall never bothered to bring a lunch or go out for meals while on the job. Charley was careful, however, to double his lunch to take care of Hall's appetite during the course of this protracted experiment. It is Bradley's recollection that Hall, on occasion, would make the trip from East St. Louis, Illinois, to Niagara Falls without bothering to eat on the train or even use the berth, preferring to sit up and work during the trip.

One spring, just before leaving for Europe, Hall gave his bicycle to Bradley who appreciated the gift and rode it for some time. He tired of bicycling, however, and passed it on to Billy Neubauer. When Hall returned from his trip, he asked for the bicycle. Hall was annoyed to think that Bradley didn't appreciate the gift and exclaimed, "Well—that is the last bicycle I am ever going to give you." But it wasn't, for Hall gave him two other bicycles before he gave up the use of bicycles as a means of transportation.

The twentieth century was greeted with optimism by business in the United States. The gold standard was fortified by legislative act and a period of general prosperity seemed assured. Corporations were making the headlines with stories of big profits and mergers which were making business even bigger. The little Pittsburgh Reduction Company was not worried about the Sherman Anti-Trust Act, for the Hall process gave it a patent-protected monopoly. Public opinion, however, was becoming alarmed at the concentration of power in big corporations, and the Roosevelt administration was engaged in a struggle to bring the situation under control through the Anti-Trust Act. The Supreme Court decision of 1904 which declared the merger of railroad interests into the Northern Securities Company to be illegal, was a shock to the business community. The "rich man's panic" of 1904 lasted a year, but it did not injure The Pittsburgh Reduction Company. Arthur V. Davis was general manager and handled the company's business with confidence and skill. The company paid its regular dividend of six dollars a year and in November increased its capitalization, and added a stock dividend of 100 per cent. The stockholders also received the right to purchase one share of the new stock at $100 for each 2.6 shares of the old stock. The aluminum business prospered with the general recovery which began in 1905; and the regular six-dollar dividend was paid with a year-end extra of three dollars.

One small way in which Hall obtained pleasure from his aluminum dividends was by attendance at concerts and operas, and one of the attractions of a trip to New York was good music. Mr. Colby has told an amusing episode that occurred on one of these occasions:

"I, too, have listened to his classical music when I am afraid my soul craved ragtime. Mr. Hall used to come to New York quite often. At that time I was in charge of the New York office. He was very fond of Grand Opera, and it was just after he started to get a considerable income from his aluminum company stock and his increased salary. He had the habit of inviting me to go to the opera with him. One time I had been up practically all of the previous night, and the opera in question was one of Wagner's. In the middle of the first act I carefully put my head on Mr. Hall's shoulder and went to sleep. I do not think he ever forgave me for that, but at any rate I was never invited to the opera with him again."

The novelty of housekeeping at the Falls eventually wore off and the prosperous state of his bank account suggested to Charles that he take another long trip and vacation. He had not been abroad since the spring of 1901 when business had taken him to Europe for several weeks. So, the spring of 1906 found Hall in London, and this is what he wrote his classmates:

"London, England, May 22, 1906

"Dear Classmates:

"I am abroad for the first time in five years, taking a five weeks' vacation trip. I am leaving for Paris and Switzerland tomorrow for about two weeks and will spend two weeks more in England on returning, and sail for home about June 19th. My brother is with me.

"I still live at Niagara Falls. I have nothing to report about my family, which Anderegg asks news about. Perhaps it is for that reason that I find it hard to write a class letter. The most prominent common ground and interest between the different members of the class, I think, is in their families. Each one can tell about the children and how interesting and bright they are—that is those who have children can—and all the others, those who have children particularly, will be greatly interested; but I have no such resource. I have, of course, my own interests, my work and business, which has been very prosperous the past year, but that is

211

shop. Among other things in this line, we have bought a large power canal and power plant at Massena, N. Y., not far from Tom Jones' old home, full of engineering and other problems and possibilities of the most interesting kind, that is, interesting to me.

"Then I might write about the fine and beautiful things which I am seeing in London and which I have come to appreciate and enjoy during the last few years, the colors of Titian, the great master of colors in painting, looking down from the walls of galleries through more than four hundred years. The wonderful portraits of Reynolds and Gainsborough. I saw the other day a Persian carpet dated 1540, said to be the finest weaving of its kind in the world. During the past year I have become interested in the Chinese porcelains, made two or three hundred years ago and earlier, the quality of which the moderns are unable to touch.

"I enjoyed the class reunion last summer extremely. I am in favor of reunions as often as possible. They are much more satisfactory than class letters.

Very cordially yours,

Charles M. Hall"

Two years later, he told more about the trip—the visit to Switzerland:

"So we went to Meiringen, or rather stopped over there on the way to Lucerne. . . . We walked through the gorge of the Aar, and climbed up to the Reichenbach Fall where Sherlock Holmes and his deadly enemy, Mr. Moriarty, met their fate until Conan Doyle resuscitated the former."

Charles was an avid follower of the adventures of Mr. Holmes and would have enjoyed helping him solve *The Singu-*

lar Affair of the Aluminum Crutch. By a singular coincidence, Dr. Conan Doyle and Charles Martin Hall both made their greatest invention in the year 1886. For Doyle it was the creation of Sherlock Holmes, and for Hall it was his aluminum process. Returning, however, to Switzerland:

"I enjoyed my stay at Interlaken more than at any other place in all my trip. The scenery is very impressive, particularly the Jungfrau, which was always beautiful, by daylight or by moonlight, white and calm, covered with snow. I think the poet Tennyson must have had the valleys about Interlaken in mind when he wrote of

'The thousand wreaths of dangling water smoke
Which, like a broken purpose, waste in air.'

Some of these streams seem to fall an even mile.

"From Lucerne we went to Bellagio on Lake Como, which is considered the most beautiful place in northern Italy; then to Milan for one day, and back by the newly opened Simplon tunnel to the Rhone Valley, and by boat to Geneva. We visited the Calvin Museum—very interesting to one who is interested in the history of the Reformation—saw the church where Calvin preached and one where John Knox preached for a time. One day we drove out to Ferney, Voltaire's home; and at another time to a place called Champel, where there is a monument with this inscription in French:

'Here perished at the stake, October 28, 1553,
Michael Servetus, aged 42.'

Servetus was a Unitarian and was executed for his opinions, and Calvin, great man though he was, was the prosecutor and persecutor. An ancient cartoon represents Calvin as heaping the faggots about Servetus which does Calvin no

213

Steam-powered dynamos in Smallman Street aluminum works, 1888

Aerial view of Aluminum Company of American hydroelectric power installation in North Carolina

injustice. It took the reformers some time to get away from the spirit of the Roman Church. Even down to our own Puritan ancestors, as I have been reading in John Fiske's *Beginnings of New England,* they were not in favor of religious liberty. They wanted liberty to worship God in their own way with the emphasis on 'their own.' But they were more humane and their persecutions were less bitter than those of their opponents; Calvin, personally, wanted Servetus beheaded; and liberty did arise as a kind of by-product of their rebellion and the controversies which they started."

The faith of his forefathers was strong in Charles, by nature and by training. Growing up in a parsonage with dutiful attendance at Sunday school and church made religion very real for this young man. However, as he matured in years and in experience, his penchant for independent thinking made him aware of the rift between science and fundamentalist interpretations of biblical lore. This trend was strengthened by his reading of the lives of great men who were martyrs to their beliefs. He was living in the period when the centuries of conflict between science and theology were drawing to a close. As a man of reason, he looked to science for his interpretation of nature but he still liked his religion strong. After attendance at an Easter service, Charles wrote Julia: "The music and flowers were nice, but the sermon was as weak as water." A decade later George Hall, speaking in memory of his brother, said with insight:

"The creed which found most significant expression in his works and deeds emphasized the importance and value of good character."

⤬ 17 ⤬

. . . the end came on a
Sunday afternoon

THE YEAR 1907 opened auspiciously for Hall. At the age of forty-three, his career as an inventor was paying dividends, both in cash and in the recognition accorded him as a leader in the electrochemical industry. Business was good. His little company, which produced 10,000 pounds of aluminum in its first year, was making 15,000,000 pounds a year by 1907. Starting with one small plant in Pittsburgh, their operations now extended from the bauxite mines in Arkansas and the alumina refinery in Illinois to the three aluminum works in New York State and Canada. With this impressive growth in its activities, the management decided that The Pittsburgh Reduction Company had outgrown its name. On January 1, 1907, it was changed quite appropriately to Aluminum Company of America.

The year 1907 closed ominously for business. Another money panic, the panic of 1907, struck suddenly and with crippling effect upon business. The directors of the Aluminum Company had paid a four-dollar dividend in February, but the business situation deteriorated so rapidly that in November, they decided to pass. The stockholders were notified of their wait-and-see attitude with a reassuring statement that earnings were unimpaired and that an amount sufficient to meet the dividend was in the company's treasury. Two years were to elapse before another dividend was ordered.

The horseless carriage, which was invented in 1892, had become an automobile by 1907. Hall finally decided he could afford to own one—so he gave away his last bicycle and bought a big shiny Packard. He engaged William Davidson, then an electrician at the plant, as his chauffeur. This arrangement proved so satisfactory that Davidson held the position as long as Hall lived. Hall liked to be driven to and from the aluminum works, and on occasion would take friends for a short spin through the countryside on the 20-mile drive to Lockport. He would point with pride to the big Niagara aluminum works, but few ever saw the rows of reduction pots inside where the aluminum was made. An order from the president of the company was required before a visitor could go through the works.

By the summer of 1908, Hall was ready for a long trip— the longest he ever made in his automobile. Commencement at Oberlin that year held a number of attractions for him. The college was celebrating its seventy-fifth anniversary, and he was president of the Alumni Association. With a couple of guests and Davidson driving, he set forth for Oberlin, 250 miles away, and arrived without mishap. Hall had a special interest in the dedication of the Carnegie Library, for he had contributed nine thousand dollars to establish the Charles M. Hall Fund for the special use of the library. Charles sat again in a pew at the First Congregational Church and listened attentively to the stirring music from a fine new organ—the gift of Charles Martin Hall. The dedication of the Finney Memorial Chapel must also have had special significance, for several years later Hall joined with Frederick N. Finney in giving an organ for the Chapel.

One of the technical projects on which Hall was engaged was finding means of reducing the cost of the alumina fed to the cryolite bath in the reduction pots. He had devised and patented a process of smelting bauxite with carbon in the intense heat of an electric furnace. The impurities—oxides of iron, silicon and titanium—were reduced by the carbon and formed a molten heavy metal alloy which separated from the lighter pure alumina. He was baffled, however, by the problem of recovering the alumina in a powder-like form which would dissolve quickly when stirred into the cryolite bath. Many years later, these and other details were perfected, but the process did not compete with the chemical process of refining bauxite.

Hall was also investigating the recovery of alumina from clay, and assisting him in his experiments from time to time was Earl Blough, a young chemist stationed at the company's plant in New Kensington. On a number of occasions when Blough was called to Niagara Falls, Hall asked him to stay at his home on Buffalo Avenue. On one such trip Hall and Blough were sitting on the front porch after dinner viewing Niagara Rapids, talking shop, and chatting about some of the Oriental rugs which Hall had proudly shown to his guest.

During a lull in the conversation, Hall drew from his pocket a large gold hunting case watch attached to a gold chain. Holding it in his hands contemplatively, he remarked:

"I figure this is the most valuable watch in the world,— I call it my 'million dollar watch.' "

Blough was surprised by this announcement but tried not, by word or expression, to show how incredible the statement seemed:

"Tell me about it."

Hall then proceeded to tell the story behind the watch.

"When we began to produce aluminum in the early nineties, we had little money and poor credit. On one occasion, we were badly in need of a loan to carry on operations and take care of our payroll. David Gillespie, a friend and small shareholder in the company, made arrangements for us to borrow $50,000. Out of gratitude, our directors voted him a small block of stock as a bonus. Not long ago, Mr. Gillespie gave me this watch and chain, and I still think he gave it to me in appreciation of getting the stock. By now the stock has increased so much in value that I figure this watch cost a million dollars."

The minutes of the Board of Directors for March 8, 1892, show that on that date, David Gillespie was voted one hundred shares of the company's stock for his efforts in helping The Pittsburgh Reduction Company obtain a loan of fifty thousand dollars, secured by the company's properties. In the interval between the loan incident and the gift of the watch, one hundred shares of the company's stock had grown in number and value. Even though Hall was indulging in a bit of hyperbole, the bonus stock was worth nearly a hundred thousand dollars—fair return for a gold watch.

Though Hall did not have a rugged constitution, it seemed to have survived the punishment of eccentric living habits— working, eating and sleeping or, rather, not sleeping. Dr. William H. Hodge, Hall's physician, still remembers an occasion in a Chicago hotel when Hall ordered mashed potatoes and stewed tomatoes. He mixed these well before eating and the mixture was his entire meal. However, the only serious illness Hall had during his first ten years in Niagara Falls was a siege of typhoid in the winter of '96-97, when typhoid was prevalent in the area. Hall did not escape, but with Hodge's skillful care, he made a good recovery. To complete his convalescence, Hall went to the seashore and a warmer climate to recuperate.

Hall was fortunate in having met Dr. Hodge soon after he moved to Niagara Falls. The competent manner in which Hodge treated typhoid fever gave Hall a confidence in his doctor's judgment and skill, which deepened year by year. Doctor and patient became great friends. In the fall of 1908, Hall was concerned again about himself. He told Hodge that he was worried by a feeling of general weakness which had taken possession of him. Dr. Hodge was disturbed by certain symptoms he found—particularly some enlargement of the spleen—and advised spending the winter in Florida. By spring, Hall was feeling better and signs of business recovery added a note of cheer to the situation. He wrote his classmates on May 15, 1909:

> "I have spent most of the year quietly and have been recovering from the depression in business and financial panic of over a year ago. I have my steamer ticket engaged to go to Europe on June 9. I expect to be in Germany and Norway principally and am looking forward to an interesting trip."

The trip to which Hall looked forward with such anticipation turned out quite differently than planned. Hall was taken sick on the ship and Dr. Hodge, of course, was beyond reach.

222

Charles wrote Julia that: "It was lying down on my back for three days on the steamer, and being treated for kidney disease which I did not have at all, which brought on my entire attack, besides being experimented with by ignorant doctors."

When he reached England, Hall lost no time in cabling Hodge to come quickly. Dr. Hodge kept his bag packed for such emergencies and arrived twelve days later. He found Hall weak but not seriously ill. Within a day or so, Hodge and Hall consulted Sir William Osler who was then professor of medicine at Oxford. The afternoon was spent with examinations and tests and that evening they joined the Oslers at dinner. Osler agreed with Hodge's diagnosis of Banti's disease and suggested the surgical removal of the spleen as the best treatment. To have Dr. Osler, one of the greatest physicians of the time, confirm Dr. Hodge's diagnosis, strengthened Hall's conviction that Hodge was the doctor he could trust.

After a short rest Hodge and Hall returned to New York, arriving on July 23. Hall was much stronger than when he left England, and went to Lake Placid Club for a couple of weeks' rest while Hodge made arrangements for the operation. He wrote Julia:

"Dr. Hodge finds that my anemia has so far disappeared that I can go anywhere, so he is arranging for me to go to Mayo Brothers, Rochester, Minn., who are the best surgeons in the world. Dr. Hodge will go with me and has engaged a most excellent nurse, Miss Bliss, for four years superintendent of the hospital at Niagara Falls."

Before starting west for this critical operation, Charles received good news from Arthur Davis, which he passed on to Julia:

223

"I find that business is very good with our company. Mr. Davis expects that we can resume dividends on the common stock this fall, and there may be a general stock distribution insuring dividends at an increased rate."

Hodge and Hall, accompanied by two nurses, left for Rochester and the Mayos in a private railway car on August 5. The operation was performed successfully, but the post-operative course was stormy for several days. Hall's courage and will to live finally turned the scales and his condition began to improve. A month later, he returned to Niagara Falls by train with his two nurses. He was soon convalescent from the operation and felt enough better to return to work.

Back at the turn of the century, Charles had taken a look in his crystal ball when he wrote Julia:

"Well, I have been doing a little prophesying on the basis of present business and prospects and tell Mr. Davis that in six years we should have works from fifteen to twenty times the present in size, and be making 100 million pounds of aluminum per year."

Statistically, he overshot the mark but the record shows his optimism was justified. In the ten years following, aluminum production was increased almost fifteenfold—from three million to forty-four million pounds per year.

Mr. Davis' prediction of increased dividends was realized also, for on November 15 the stockholders of Aluminum Company of America received a 500 per cent stock dividend; each share of stock was increased to five. At the same time arrangements were made to retire the six thousand shares of preferred stock which were issued in 1899. Sold at par, they were redeemed at $150 a share.

224

Charles Martin Hall at the age of forty-two

On February 17, 1910, Mr. Davis was elected president of the company and dividends on the common stock were resumed. The first quarterly dividend on the new stock was one dollar per share. That, of course, was equal to a twenty-dollar annual dividend on the old stock. To Hall, it meant a yearly income of $170,000 from his aluminum stockholding. His ambition to become a rich inventor had been fulfilled. He was at the peak of his career, but his physical resources had been sadly drained.

With the coming of winter he went south, confidently hoping that rest in a moderate climate would help him regain his health. By spring he felt much better. Commencement at Oberlin in 1910 brought another honor to Hall. He was awarded an honorary doctor's degree—LL.D.—by his alma mater. The occasion took on added significance because Orville and Wilbur Wright were also honored in the same manner and at the same time. This meeting was a significant portent of what aluminum was going to mean in future development of the airplane.

Hall's next honor, and one that received international publicity, was the award of the famous Perkin Medal for his contributions to chemistry. Hall was chosen for this honor by a committee representing three societies:

American Electrochemical Society
American Chemical Society
Society of Chemical Industry (Great Britain)

The medal was presented in New York on January 20, 1911. Paul L. T. Héroult, the Frenchman who discovered how to make aluminum at about the same time as did Hall in America, crossed the ocean to help celebrate the occasion. In his acceptance speech, Hall told of his interest in aluminum

226

during school and college days. He then outlined the experiments which led to his discovery that he could produce aluminum by the electrolysis of alumina dissolved in molten cryolite. Héroult also contributed gracious remarks and recollections of his early career in France.

After the festivities were over, Hall went to Bermuda for his customary winter vacation. In May, after his return, he wrote his classmates from Niagara Falls:

"I write in a somewhat more cheerful mood than a year ago. My health is better than it was then. I realize though that I am growing old. This is the first time that I have been obliged to use glasses in writing a class letter.

"I have not been active in business or work during the past year. In the winter and spring I spent three months in Bermuda. It is a fine place to rest and do nothing. The place has many attractions, but one exhausts them after a month or two. I kept house in Bermuda and found my neighbors—Bermudians—most courteous and hospitable. I expect to spend some of the summer in a cottage on Lake Keuka (Finger Lakes, New York)."

As his health improved, his impatience to get back to his experiments increased. He had so many projects planned, that he began to fear he might leave this world before he finished them. His trip to the Mayos' was a constant reminder of the uncertainties of life. Hall put the situation realistically when he wrote: "My doctor talks optimistically, but I suppose it is his business to talk so." Hall was to learn soon what an implacable foe he carried in his system.

Later in the year, Dr. Hodge received another urgent summons from Hall, in New York on a business trip. On occasion, Hall would become unduly alarmed by mild upsets and Hodge could never be sure of the importance his patient was attaching to his current symptoms. He had formed the habit of keeping a bag packed just in case the next summons might be a real "crisis." Hodge left at once for New York and his preliminary examination indicated acute appendicitis. Two specialists were called in for consultation and they confirmed the diagnosis. Dr. Henry C. Buswell of Buffalo was called to New York at once to perform the operation.

The operation disclosed a critical situation—a massive hemorrhage in the area of the appendix and not an inflamed appendix. Hall was in shock following the operation and for several days was not expected to live. His condition improved, however, and a month later he was able to return to Niagara Falls accompanied by two nurses.

Hall's attempts to transmute elements—to make rhodium or platinum out of iron—started in 1896. A letter to Julia in 1904 disclosed the fact that he was still working on this "enormous scheme." At home again in 1911, after the operation, Hall told William Hoopes, trusted friend and chief electrical engineer of the company, about his efforts to make rhodium. Hoopes had worked with Hall on a number of projects and Hall was impressed with his flair for research. Hall took Hoopes into his confidence because he was afraid he might have another attack and die before the experiments were completed. After Hall's passing, Hoopes told Arthur Davis something of these conversations:

"Mr. Hall had formed theories, based upon these experiments, that the transmutation of metals, and conversion of matter from one form to another were perfectly possible. He asked me to repeat his experiments, in order to confirm them and after his death to publish his work and the conclusions he drew from it. . . . The important thing is that during the

228

conversations regarding this work, Mr. Hall revealed that probably his chief ambition in life was to make some discovery which would be revolutionary with regard to the present conception of the constitution of matter and which would be of immense benefit to mankind."

Hall decided to try Pasadena, California, for the next winter vacation. He made the trip in comfort, resting on a hospital bed set up in the private railway car of William Taft. He took his chauffeur and had his Packard shipped to the coast by freight. No long trips were contemplated, but Hall found pleasure in short jaunts to San Diego and near-by places. Dr. and Mrs. Hodge came to California and stayed for a time with Hall at his house on South Orange Grove Avenue. In the spring of 1913, Hall wrote his classmates:

"The last two years I have spent principally in being ill. I have had some unusual experiences. Several times the doctors have expected me to die, and once I was told that I was about to die. One sometimes wonders how he would feel in the face of such an announcement and how the future would appear to him. Bacon says, 'Men fear death as children fear in the dark, and as that natural fear in children is increased with tales so is the other.' In my own case there was no fear. My vitality at that particular time was so low that the prospect of rest seemed most attractive and I was more interested in trying to get my affairs in shape to leave than anything else. I had hardly thought of the future at all or of the things that are supposed to seem particularly important at such times, except 'from childly use and ancient wont,' as Tennyson says.

"While strength remains in any degree one hates to leave this beautiful world, and at times I was apprehensive and nervous when the prospect presented itself. I believe there are some grounds for thinking and hoping that personal existence continues after death, but to me, as I believe to a great many thinking people, that belief or hope is very vague and shadowy. We simply do not know.

"My severe illness brought one consolation in that it showed I had some very good and faithful friends.

"The winter of 1911-12 I spent in southern California, last winter in Bermuda. My health improved considerably during six months in the latter place and lately I have had a hope that I might have good health again.

"I have moved across the street from where I lived for ten years and can now look out on the flowing rapids of the Niagara, and I have night and day the constant background of the sound of rushing waters. It is very soothing and musical."

Charles left for Bermuda in November, 1912. Although this trip was for rest and relaxation, Hall was soon busy writing letters to his associates in the company. In the files are found ten letters from Hall in Paget West, Bermuda, dated between November 30 and January 13. These letters start with instructions to Messrs. Moritz and Doerschuk on changes to be made in an experimental carbon baking furnace. The next letter, on December 2, entreated the office to put sufficient postage on their letters—he was tired of having his mail delayed by insufficient postage. Also he wanted all of his regular papers and magazines forwarded including *Popular Science Monthly* and *Science*. Then followed more letters about the carbon baking furnace and an aluminum nitride furnace.

This series closed with five long letters dealing with the company's future supply of the pure carbon required for the anodes in the reduction pots and for furnace linings. Hall told Mr. Moritz that he had "been giving this matter considerable thought for the last ten or fifteen years" and thought the company should be doing more to ensure adequate supplies in the future.

All of these letters were written longhand by his niece and signed by Charles. In most of them were interlineations in Charles's own handwriting. The letter dictated the day after Christmas made seven typed pages when copied and was a comprehensive treatment of the subject under discussion. Even though these letters were dictated from an invalid's chair, they show no lack of mental alertness. During the winter in Bermuda, Hall was visited by his faithful friend, Dr. Hodge.

Summer and fall of the year, Hall spent at home within sight and sound of the rushing rapids of Niagara River. Visits of classmates and other friends from Oberlin were especially pleasurable, since he could entertain them at home and take them for drives in his new car. He had sold the Packard in California and now had a handsome Pierce Arrow with an aluminum body. It was finished in black enamel so the aluminum did not show, but Hall could tell his friends with pride of this new use for aluminum.

At home, Hall still played the piano occasionally. For an ill man, he played Beethoven's Sonata Pathetique with considerable vigor and expression. More often, however, he had the player moved up to the grand piano, and he listened to his favorite music from a fine collection of piano rolls. Having records played for him on his phonograph was a fair substitute for the opera. Although the music from these devices was lacking in the tonal artistry to which his ears were accustomed, he still found entertainment in their performance. He took an absorbing interest in his books, and when especially tired, enjoyed having someone read to him. The collection of Oriental rugs continued to grow, for Hall found plenty of time for their inspection and purchase during periods of convalescence. In the aluminum business, there were many things to keep Hall's mind active, and he followed closely current operations and experimental projects in which he was interested.

When wintry winds began to whistle through Niagara, Hall knew it was time to leave. Although he never felt quite at home in California, he decided to try it again. By November he was again on South Orange Grove Avenue in Pasadena. The climate in general was satisfactory he wrote, but how it could rain!

"The winter here has been pleasant for the most part. One of the remarkable features of this country is the way in which it can rain when it does rain . . . I like Bermuda better and if I go away next winter, I am thinking now of either spending the winter in Bermuda or trying the south coast of England."

Hall had another serious attack during the winter, but he gradually recovered and by the time spring rolled around he felt "almost the same as before."

Each spring found Hall optimistic regarding his chances for regaining health. But year by year and month by month, the enemy within was sapping his vitality. In appearance, he still retained traces of the youthful characteristics which were so prominent at the prime of life. But he was a man in whom, as Julia said, illness had wrought sad ravages in face and figure. The diagnosis of Banti's disease was sufficient for the time, but modified in the light of subsequent findings it seems certain that Hall was in the grip of one of the leukemias. The prognosis was unfavorable.

William A. Thomas, since 1904, had served as Hall's secretary at the aluminum works. Bill became a trusted friend and visited Hall's home once a week or oftener to care for his personal accounts and papers. In many ways, Bill learned to know the real Hall and became one of his great admirers. He saw, firsthand, his concern for the welfare of the men at the works and the practical ways in which he expressed this interest. In the spring of '14, the company needed the accounting skills of Thomas to organize a system at New Kensington and on May 15, Bill went to Hall's home to say good-by. There was an undercurrent of sadness in the meeting and Bill left with the feeling that this might mean farewell.

Several months later, Hall called Homer Johnson to Niagara Falls on a special mission. He had decided to make important changes in his will, and his old friend and classmate was the only attorney he would trust with this task. Johnson had become a national figure and was known as an authority on constitutional law. Hall explained the changes he had in mind and Johnson went to work on the new document. After the preliminary drafts had been revised and approved, the final copy was duly signed and witnessed on the 1st of November. The next day, Homer and Charles just visited. As Homer said:

"He seemed very much more cheerful than at some other visits I have made to him and was looking forward to his winter in Daytona with considerable anticipation. I think he expected to come home more firmly than when leaving for most other winters during the last few years."

The sight and sound of the ocean brought deep response in Charles. The music of rushing surf upon the shore gave some relief from tension even though his tormented body was beyond healing. Charles spent many hours riding upon the broad, firm sands at Daytona, and occasionally took short trips through

Aluminum reduction pots at Smallman Street, 1889

inland woods and field. However, some of the problems that Charles seemed to have left behind were with him in Florida. On December 16, he dictated a two-page letter to the Niagara works. It started with the sentence "I wish to suggest some experiments in the line of purifying coke and other carbon materials for use as raw materials in making carbon anodes." In the letter was a sketch of the apparatus he suggested and explicit directions for the conduct of the work. The letter closed with this injunction: "Kindly preserve this letter carefully, and acknowledge receipt of it and let me know what you can do."

That was Charles's last message to his associates. Just a week later he was stricken. Dr. Hodge was summoned but found there was little he could do. Charles was in a coma and did not recognize his good friend at his bedside. Life ebbed slowly, and the end came on a Sunday afternoon, December 27, 1914.

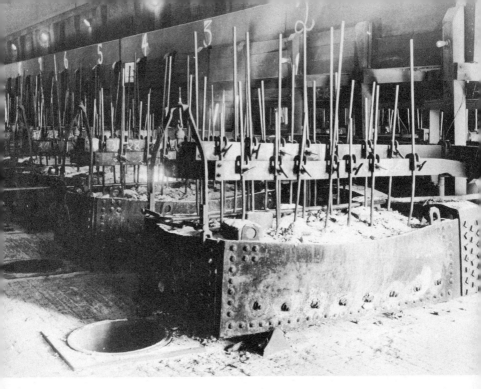

Aluminum reduction pots at Massena, New York, 1914

Modern pot room, Aluminum Company of America

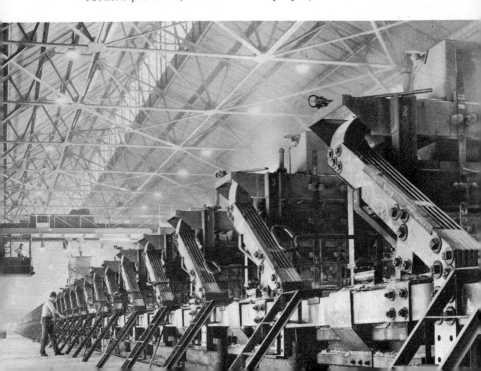

Memorial services were held in the First Congregational Church of Oberlin on the 22nd of January, to pay tribute to this man who had become Oberlin's First Citizen. It was in the spirit of the gathering to have music from the organ given to the church by Hall.

George Hall spoke with pride of his serious-minded brother whose school and college days were filled with dreams of discoveries which would enrich the world.

Julia Hall contributed an eyewitness account of Charles's famous discovery in the family woodshed, how she thrilled to the sight of the first shining button of aluminum.

Arthur Davis recalled his first meeting with Hall in a boardinghouse in Pittsburgh, and traced his career from the little plant with five men on Smallman Street to a company with many plants and ten thousand employees. Davis testified to Hall's scientific skills and the many discoveries he made to develop his aluminum process and build an industry. He spoke with intimate knowledge of the young inventor's persistence and determination, of his abiding faith in the aluminum process which eventually brought him a fortune.

Homer Johnson, classmate and confidant, emphasized the loyalties that characterized the man—loyalty to his family and friends, loyalty to his college and classmates, loyalty to his work and associates.

William Hodge wrote with feeling of his friend and patient. He told of Hall's love of the beautiful in art and nature, his unselfish character, and his earnest desire to live so that he might solve new problems for the benefit of humanity.

Henry Churchill King, president of Oberlin College, expressed pride in their distinguished alumnus and trustee. Hall's previous gifts to college and town—some two hundred thou-

236

sand dollars—were already known. King announced that Hall's will provided magnificent bequests for education; the gift to Oberlin was estimated at over three million dollars.

Before composing his last will, Hall spent many hours in contemplation of the form and substance which his major bequests should take. Just as industry was realizing the material benefits of low-cost aluminum which his process had brought to America, Hall sought ways in which his fortune could be used to bring lasting benefits to humanity. His decision was to promote the cause of higher education.

Hall sensed that he would be leaving this world at the start of a new industrial era, initiated by such inventions as his own aluminum process, the telephone, radio, the airplane and other marvels which would bring distant lands and people together and bring new problems for youth to solve. The ominous reverberations of the great struggle in Europe were heralding world war, and Hall recognized that the world would need educated leaders if its economic, social and political problems were to be solved.

Free enterprise and a good education, which let him make the most of opportunity, had endowed him with a fortune. Having neither wife nor children, he decided to make tens of thousands of young men and women his heirs. The results of these decisions were revealed by his last will and testament.

When the will was opened and read, his munificent gifts were disclosed. There were bequests to family and friends not previously cared for. Then came Oberlin:

> Two hundred thousand dollars—an endowment fund—the income to be used for development and maintenance of the campus and other college grounds, the arboretum and the forestry preserves.

Five hundred thousand dollars—for an auditorium—a memorial to Hall's mother, Sophronia Brooks Hall.

One hundred thousand dollars—a fund for maintenance of the auditorium.

One third of the residuary estate—a general endowment fund for operation of the college, but not for buildings.

Arthur V. Davis and Homer Johnson were made executors of the estate and trustees of the residuary estate and special bequests. They were instructed by the terms of the will to conserve the shares of Aluminum Company of America during the lifetime of the trust, which could be fifteen years. The income and eventually the assets of the residuary fund were to be divided as follows:

One-third to Oberlin College; one-sixth to Berea College; one-sixth to the American Missionary Association; and one-third to be used by the trustees for educational purposes in the following foreign countries—Japan, continental Asia, Turkey and the Balkan states in Europe. No part of these funds was to be used for the purpose of instruction in theology for Hall believed that there were others sufficiently interested in that work to carry on without his assistance. It was with uncanny foresight that Hall selected these particular foreign countries as ones which would have great need for higher education to train truly democratic leaders.

Oberlin College received only the income from its share of the residuary estate until the year 1925. Then the capital assets were divided and the college set up the Charles M. Hall Endowment fund with its share. The balance of the estate was finally distributed to other beneficiaries in accordance with the will, and the estate closed in 1928. The trustees were faced with a great responsibility in selecting the schools in foreign lands, which were to share the final third of the estate. After extensive investigation, twenty-two universities, colleges and educational boards were chosen. Their activities were located in Albania, Bulgaria, Greece, Macedonia, Turkey in Europe, Turkey in Asia, Lebanon, India, China, Japan and Korea. The bequests varied—some large, some small—depending on competency and need; and the gifts were all managed by American and British trustees.

Although the six hundred thousand dollars for the auditorium at Oberlin was received a few years after Hall's death, construction was not started until 1951. Carefully invested by the Oberlin trustees, the fund grew to two million dollars in the intervening years. Two-thirds of this was used for the building and the remainder set up as a fund for its maintenance. Wallace K. Harrison, the architect, planned a building to serve all the dramatic arts. It is uniquely functional in design, with stage, theater workshop and drama classrooms. The auditorium has seats for 500 and will be used also for recitals, concerts, lectures, debates and other town and college gatherings.

The striking white Vermont marble serpentine front, and the unusual angles and graceful curves of the structure stimulate the imagination. Two great limestone wings flank the entrance and welcome the visitor. Carved on one of these walls according to Hall's instructions is this inscription:

In loving Memory of
SOPHRONIA BROOKS HALL
This building was
erected by her son
CHARLES M. HALL

239

At the time the auditorium was dedicated, a published statement said that Hall's gifts to the college had amounted to twenty million dollars. The Charles M. Hall Endowment Fund provides the financial backbone for an educational program which justifies the donor's plans and hopes for his alma mater.

On a quiet tree-shaded plot in Oberlin's Westwood Cemetery is a granite monolith bearing the simple inscription:

HALL

There rests the mortal Charles Martin Hall. His woodshed laboratory on College Street is gone—but what he created there endures. The Immortal Woodshed has earned its name.

Epilogue

. . . GETTING TO KNOW CHARLES MARTIN HALL

I never met Mr. Hall in person, but have spent thirty-five years getting acquainted with the man. I was a year out of college when Hall died, and was getting my indoctrination in research at the splendid laboratories of National Bureau of Standards in Washington. I did not have to meet the challenge of a woodshed laboratory as did Hall. Five years later I started my career in aluminum research with the Aluminum Company of America, which I shall call Alcoa. From then on, I was to hear the old-timers telling stories about Charlie Hall.

In 1941, a fortunate day spent in Rochester with Charles's youngest sister, Miss Louie Hall, brought forth clear-cut recollections of the famous woodshed at the family home in Oberlin. Miss Louie, a sprightly spinster of seventy-one, had presented to Alcoa the collection of letters from Charles to Julia and other members of the family, letters which Julia had preserved so carefully. From this point on, my ambition to write the life story of Hall began to crystallize.

In the early '20s, I met Charles's niece, Yeoli Stimson Acton, at the Shawinigan aluminum works where her husband, Edward H. Acton, was superintendent. Now retired, the Actons live in Stockbridge, Massachusetts. During a recent visit with them, Yeoli loaned precious daguerreotypes of her grandfather and grandmother, Heman and Sophronia Hall, and of her Uncle Charles. To the Actons, I am deeply indebted for their help and interest in this biography.

Homer Johnson, a resident of New London, Ohio, was a classmate and lifelong friend of both Hall and Josephine Cody. Making the acquaintance of this genial gentleman of plus ninety years has been one of the very pleasant experiences of my life. His contributions to my acquaintanceship with Hall have been invaluable.

Dr. William Hodge was Hall's personal physician for the last twenty years of his life. Dr. Hodge still enjoys the good health he worked so hard to preserve in Hall. His personal recollections of his friend and patient have been most helpful.

Donald M. Love, the secretary of Oberlin College, has furnished information as well as photographs from the files of Oberlin College Library. Both Mr. Love and Professor Robert S. Fletcher, who wrote the authoritative volumes, *A History of Oberlin College,* have taken a deep interest in advising on various phases of the Oberlin scene.

With Alcoa, there are still many who knew and worked with Hall, and these men have been most helpful in my pleasant task of reconstructing his life story. Captain Hunt's son, Roy, now chairman of the Executive Committee of Alcoa has given wholehearted support to this biographical project. The recollections of Arthur V. Davis, telling of his long and close association with Hall, have been drawn upon.

To his secretary, William A. Thomas, and to his chauffeur,

William Davidson, Hall was always a great man who commanded their respect and received their devoted service. They have responded repeatedly to my questioning. Charles Bradley is another old-timer who has contributed bits of lore about the early days of the company. Victor Doerschuk, an Oberlin graduate, started his career in the aluminum industry when he reported for work at the Niagara Falls plant in 1910; he helped Mr. Hall on some of his experimental work. Joe Taylor, another old-timer, has also furnished information and stories of the early days which have been important in adding color and accuracy to these pages.

In addition to the letters Charles wrote to Julia and the family, I have read numerous communications to Captain Hunt, to Arthur Davis and to other associates in the company. Alcoa's archivist, Chester C. Conner, has been most helpful in gathering these documents and letters from the company's works and from forgotten files. Most of these letters have to do with the business of the company and are without general interest. There are many, however, which deal with the technical problems of the company and give detailed directions and sketches for carrying out experiments looking to their solution. They give graphic proof of the incessant activity of this inventor's fertile mind. Even when the end of life seemed near, Hall was making arrangements with a trusted associate to have certain of his cherished projects carried to conclusion.

The search for the complete Charles Martin Hall has been a fascinating one. It is the hope of his biographer that, through this work, the man from Ohio who brought aluminum to America will become better known to the people of America.

Junius Edwards